My Big

C

Still Here After All These Years

THE ORIGINAL STORY

My Big

Still Here After All These Years

C

NANCY F. RADIN

DRAMEDY PRESS

A portion of the profits from this book will be donated to LivingBeyondStatistics.org or other cancer causes.

ISBN: 978-0-9986615-2-0

Cover photo by David Greitzer (www.davidgreitzer.com)
Cover design, interior design by JM Shubin, Book Alchemist (www.bookalchemist.net)

Disclaimer

The story I am about to tell is based on fact. However, I have slightly simplified certain events for clarity, and changed minor details such as identifying characteristics, places, times, and names to avoid defaming or insulting the people and institutions involved. The point of my story is not to say how badly anyone in my story behaved, but to record how as a Stage 4 cancer patient I was challenged in many ways, both during my diagnosis with terminal cancer and since. It is to show how I began writing about my life in 2006, and never used or infringed on anyone else's story. Most importantly, it is to illustrate how I am thus far surviving many of the difficult challenges thrown at me, for the purpose of giving hope to those touched by cancer or other significant challenges.

For all my Superheroes:
my family, friends, amazing doctors
and
all those touched by cancer

He who has a *why* to live for,
can bear almost any *how.*

—Friedrich Nietzsche

Contents

Preface

I first read *Man's Search for Meaning* in 2002, after I was diagnosed in my 40s with Stage 4 metastatic cancer, and given an initial eighteen-month prognosis. I was awestruck by many passages and points made in that book. Moreover, I found myself completely desperate to find some "meaning" in what was happening to me and, consequently, to my family.

The book's author, Dr. Viktor Emil Frankl (1905–1997), was a noted Austrian neurologist and psychiatrist. He was also the founder of Logotherapy, a form of Existential Analysis, the basic premise of which is "*Life has meaning under all circumstances, even the most miserable ones.*" It is our job as individuals to find meaning in our lives.

Frankl came to that conclusion because of—and in spite of—his having spent three years as a prisoner in Auschwitz, Dachau, and other concentration camps. He had sewn the only copy of his book into the lining of his coat, which he thought the Nazis would not find if he were captured. Little did he know that he would be would be stripped of all of his clothes when he arrived at the camp.

Scrapping together pieces of paper and a worn pencil, he spent much of his time in the camps rewriting his book from scratch and from memory, chronicling his time and observations of life in the camps. Though his pregnant wife and parents perished in the camps, Frankl miraculously survived. After being freed, his renowned book was finally published in 1946. By the time of Dr. Frankl's death in 1997, the book had sold over 10 million copies, was translated into 24 languages, and is considered to be one of the 10 most influential books ever published in the United States.

According to Frankl's Logotherapy, meaning in one's life can be discovered in three ways. The first way is through the *attitude* we take towards unavoidable suffering. "In some way, suffering ceases to be suffering at the moment it finds meaning."

The notion that one's life requires meaning or purpose was a concept I had already embraced on many levels: as a parent, teacher, writer, and director. Artists have an innate and intense understanding, perhaps more than others, that all things in life are dealt to us for a purpose and have meaning. Our highest highs and lowest lows become the substance of that which we create with our God-given talents.

Frankl explained the concept of *servitude* as a second path to discovering one's meaning through "creating a work or doing a deed," or in other words, service to a higher purpose by giving rather than taking. Having spent a great deal of my life in service to help others was something I have always cherished and loved to do. As artists, we compulsively pour our hearts and souls into our work to communicate and illuminate life as we understand it. No matter how insurmountable I have found life's struggles at times, I instinctively also found that helping others eased my pain and gave those struggles a sense of purpose.

Last but not least, Frankl believed that meaning could be found thru *loving* another human being. My life had always been filled with an abundance of love for my children, whom I adored, a husband of 25 years, my extended family, friends, and countless students. Loving would be the easiest part for me, or so I thought.

Armed with copious amounts of unconditional love for others, I understood that I needed to create and to serve, and to accept my unavoidable suffering in an "honorable" way, by finding meaning in it. In doing so, I felt hopeful that I would be able to move forward with what remained of my life in a purposeful way.

As Frankl interpreted Nietzsche's famous statement, by having a *"why"* to live for, I would try to bear this overwhelming *"how."*

And so, my journey began.

Nancy F. Radin

info@nradin.com

Introduction

"Big Blue Buses"

As I stepped off the curb with my little service dog, Allie, and onto Wilshire Boulevard in Los Angeles, a big blue transit bus seemed to careen out of nowhere right towards me. My dog reacted quickly and pulled me back onto the sidewalk. At that moment in the summer of 2010, my life changed forever, how much so I would not know for several weeks.

As I regained my balance, I noticed the entire side of the bus was plastered with an advertisement for a brand new cable TV series about cancer, which I had vaguely heard about. A certain well-known and attractive celebrity, whom I will call "Candy," was posing lying on a beach with an hourglass running out of sand. It was a curious image, yet strangely familiar.

"Wow, that's bizarre!" I thought, reacting more to the image on the bus than the fact that I had almost been hit. A second blue bus drove by several minutes later. This time Candy was in a swimming pool but with the same cancer-show logo, and it felt as if she were smirking specifically at me.

"I don't believe it!" I blurted out loud. This was too close for comfort, and the coincidence felt eerie.

Within a matter of days, the buses seemed to multiply like randy rabbits. One bus quickly turned into 10, which turned into dozens, and it was now starting to feel creepy. I began to dislike the buses, as did my companion dog, who was always keenly aware when I was troubled.

Then one day, as another blue bus with Candy in yet a different pose passed by, my dog looked at me as if she couldn't believe it. She started barking at the bus and began to chase it. As I grabbed tight on her leash, it hit me like a ton of bricks.

I know Candy. *I am Candy!*

My Big

C

Diagnosis

No one was there to take me home from the hospital, so I took myself home to die.

"Get your affairs in order and say goodbye to the kids," one of the doctors told me.

Only six months earlier, in mid-2002, I had been diagnosed with early Stage 1 cancer, which is considered treatable and non-life-threatening.

The unpleasant recommendation was a double mastectomy, because the previous year I'd had a precancerous lesion in my other breast. I didn't want to deal with this fear or life-threatening risk any longer. I had been suffering with Lupus, too, for many years, which made the possibility of new surgeries much more difficult. But most importantly, I had two teenagers I wasn't about to leave motherless.

"I want a PET scan before we go any further," I told the surgeon, knowing that I was not a candidate for reconstructive surgery. I wasn't a doctor, but I certainly knew that it was routine to rule out all other medical issues before sending a patient to surgery.

The new PET scans were used to detect cancers throughout the body, and to me it was obvious that you can't—or shouldn't—properly treat a person unless you know the correct stage of their disease.

"As I've already told you, the chances of your cancer having spread are practically zero," he said rather cavalierly.

"*Practically*," I pronounced deliberately, "then chances do still exist. So I want the scan." I was adamant.

"How do you even know what a PET scan is?"

His tone was insulting and condescending. "I've done my homework," I replied confidently.

My insistence was based on the countless hours of research I had spent on the newly developed Internet with the enormous help of my sister, Lara, who lived in Virginia. I also had a number of discussions with my cousin, Ron, a radiologist at Cedars-Sinai in Los Angeles. *God bless them both!*

The surgeon continued, "I am also obligated to tell you that your insurance might not cover it. It's a new and very expensive test."

I remained unflinching as a gut feeling kept nagging at me. I was prepared to have my breasts sawed off, if necessary, but not if it wouldn't help my chances of survival. When faced with the possibility of death, you simply do what you have to do. But, you have to know the enemy. It's a no-brainer!

"Whatever...I'll pay if insurance doesn't, and deal with the insurance company later." I didn't understand why it would be a problem. Fortunately, I had great insurance.

Through clenched teeth, I said, "Just order the PET, please."

"Fine. We'll do it for your *neurosis*. I'll schedule it for tomorrow." He practically spit out the word as he relented and hung up.

"*Neurosis?*" Aghast, I slammed the phone down. I couldn't get that word out of my mind, and loathed his use of it. It felt like a betrayal of trust for a doctor to not be 100-percent certain before allowing me to go through major surgery.

Just then, I could swear I felt my father's gentle hands on my shoulders, proud that I had not allowed myself to be intimidated. I knew, if he were still here, that he above all others would understand the nagging feeling in my gut which I couldn't shake, that the cancer might have already spread despite the doctors telling me it hadn't. My hope was to disprove this feeling. One way or the other I needed to be sure, so that I could get the proper treatment.

There was one thing, however, of which I was utterly and absolutely certain. I would do everything I could to stay alive, not only for myself but even more for the sake of my two teenaged kids. I would do everything for their sake. Moreover, as their mom, I wasn't finished with them yet. They weren't fully baked!

The following morning, having been instructed not to eat or drink anything before my test, I was psyched and felt empowered as I drove back over the Golden Gate Bridge from Marin into San Francisco for my hard-fought PET scan. I felt confident that the miracles of modern medicine would set me on the right path.

Then, I wove my way through Golden Gate Park. Left turns are infuriatingly illegal almost everywhere in San Francisco, so I hung three rights instead onto California towards the hospital. I drove around for half an hour just to find a parking place, which is another notorious and ridiculously expensive headache in San Francisco.

When I finally arrived at the Nuclear Medicine Department, the very name on the door sent a shiver of fear through me. As I pushed the door open, I knew from my research that a radioactive material called FDG would be shot into a vein in my arm and that it would travel through my blood collecting in organs and tissues. The image was frightening, but at least I knew what I would be facing. A kindly technician helped me up on the scan table, a cold, hard surface that slid through a large donut-looking machine for roughly an hour, during which I was told to remain perfectly still.

Afterwards, the results were not shared with me, a common practice in those days.

Next, I was sent to another department for a bone scan, which was somewhat alarming. I was beginning to feel like a suitcase on a conveyor belt being tracked and scanned at the airport.

In the second room, I was greeted by another pleasant technician who arrived with what looked like a small bank vault box in which one would keep jewelry. Inside the "vault" another protective tube contained a radioactive isotope, which he handled with the utmost caution, as if he were dealing with Ebola virus. It too was injected into a vein in my arm.

I was then sent to a room to wait for *four long hours* while this poisonous substance traveled to the bone cells. After that, I was placed on a different kind of hard table and told again to remain still. A scanner then slowly moved over me in tiny increments the full length of my body, and then under me as well.

As I lay on the machine, I strained my eyes all the way to the right to observe the radiologist, a young Asian woman, through the glass wall. The process was much like watching pre-digital photographs develop, bathing in chemicals while images slowly appeared on photo paper. It was fascinating to watch—*until* she began to carefully examine numerous dark spots, which came more into focus.

As I studied the spots, I was not significantly alarmed because they were exactly where the orthopedist had told me for the last few years that the pain I was having was from the onset of arthritis: in my shoulder, lower back, and hip. But then I noticed the largest of all the spots was in the middle of my chest, which, though I'm not a doctor, seemed to be an odd spot for arthritis. But what do I know?

The radiologist stared at that particular spot the longest, and I could see her enlarge the image several times. I was about to yell out "it's just arthritis," but she whipped out a red pen and circled that spot, along with all the others. My worst nightmare appeared to happen right before my very eyes, but I kept telling myself it was just arthritis. Then she was gone.

I suddenly felt as if my head had slipped off my body. I was listening without hearing, looking without seeing, touching without feeling, and nothing was coming out of my mouth. I felt dizzy. I think the technician then helped me off the table and said some things, but I didn't hear a word.

He could tell I was disoriented as he handed me a paper stamped "STAT," which I knew meant "urgent," and a small map. He drew a blue line on the map from where I was standing and also circled the "Medical Records" department, where I was now supposed to go. It was located somewhere on the other side of the huge building. He also wrote "by 5 p.m." as his mouth shaped the word "hurry."

I was now also feeling hypoglycemic from not having eaten all day. I left the office feeling dizzier by the moment as I made my way through the mazelike building. I began to feel like I was a little mouse running through a lab test. Each hallway led to another, which eventually took me to a dead end, no pun intended. Needless to say, following the blue line in my condition and finding the records room was not easy.

As I passed a candy machine, shaking from hunger, I dropped in some quarters, which got stuck, and I pounded on every button, but nothing came out. I suddenly remembered a granola bar, which I pulled from my purse. With stomach grumbling, I scarfed it down, leaving a trail of crumbs as I made my way down the long corridor. Somehow, I managed to make it to the records room with only minutes to spare before it closed.

I opened the heavy, windowless door and was pleased to see just one young man at the counter.

"Not bad," I thought, until I noticed the half a dozen others sitting in chairs against the walls. There was only one person at the counter to help.

"God...I can't believe this," I said to myself. Others were grumbling to themselves too, and everyone was impatiently watching the clock. I tiptoed around the others. Some people shot me nasty looks, but I pretended not to see them.

"Excuse me," I said politely to the woman behind the counter. "I have a quick question—"

"There are no quick questions," she said, rudely. "Take a number. Have a seat and wait for your number to be called."

The monster caught me off guard. I expected her to be helpful like the others. I sighed and looked around the room.

"Excuse me, where did you say the numbers are?"

"I didn't. They're by the door."

I turned towards the door and saw there were no numbers left in the holder.

"Excuse me, ma'am. I don't see any numbers."

"Can't you see I am helping someone else?"

As if in one of the old myths about monsters lurking in the center of the labyrinth, mine looked intimidating as I tried to get her attention. When she finally looked up, I could tell right then that things were not going to go well.

"Yes, I'm very sorry," I said, keeping it cool. "I just want to know where I can find a number so I can sit down and wait until you call me, so I can ask you a simple question about picking up—"

"Are you hearing impaired?"

"What? No!"

"Then why are you pretending to be?" she sniped. I resented that. My mother was severely hearing impaired all her life.

After tangling with Dr. Neurosis, I was already in battle mode, and this was just one more battle to be fought. I wasn't going to be intimidated.

"Look, ma'am," I said. "My surgery is scheduled for first thing in the morning. The scan results are finished and waiting for me.

"I don't care. You'll have to come back tomorrow. We are closing soon. You should have come earlier."

"But I just finished the test."

The cute young hunk at the counter allowed me to go ahead of him.

"Thank you, I really appreciate it," I said coyly.

"No problem." He smiled and I melted a little.

"Ma'am, this is really urgent," I pleaded.

"Everything around here is urgent. And, I'm only one person," she shot back. Things were quickly escalating.

"It's always like this," someone shouted from the back of the room.

"But, the results will determine whether I need to go through the surgery tomorrow."

"Well, why did you wait so long?"

"I didn't. My doctor did. I just had the frigging test."

"Then I suggest you take it up with him!" I heard another person gasp.

"Listen…the results are ready, I can see them…right there…look…that envelope has my name on it, and you could just hand it…"

"TAKE A SEAT!" The evil one yelled as she slammed her fist on the counter.

How could she leave me hanging like this? *It was cruel and unusual punishment for a crime I had not committed.* I had to get those scans now…but how? I clearly wasn't getting anywhere being nice. I thought, and though I don't like to, I needed to take it up a few notches. *Enough of this crap!* I was hella mad and not taking any more of this. Fortunately, my blood sugar began to surge at that moment and along with it rose something from deep within me.

It was the "Defenseless Creature," a character from a Neil Simon play, which I have directed a number of times, who has a nervous disorder and relentlessly demands money from an ill banker, the employer of her injured husband. After pushing the banker to his absolute limits, he hands over all the money she wants, only to find out afterward that her husband never even worked for him in the first place.

"Listen, lady," I screeched as my eyes rolled back in my head. "Unless you want to take my place in the operating room tomorrow and let them take a chain saw to your chest, I need the results, NOW!"

The people on the chairs were frozen.

"NO!" she screamed back. This chick wasn't backing down.

Something else was also rising up in me, a survival instinct to the new and mounting betrayals in my life—my body and, now, the health care system. If I had to start fighting for myself, I had to start now!

"GET...ME...YOUR...SUPERVISOR!" I demanded.

"MY SUPERVISOR IS NOT HERE TODAY! COME BACK TOMORROW MORNING!" Before I knew it, I slid halfway over the counter. We were nose to nose. "Defenseless Creature" was in full throttle.

"I AM NOT COMING BACK IN THE MORNING!" I bellowed. I felt myself turning a furious red. The hunk stepped closer in solidarity.

"Give the lady her scans, please, before she passes out." Hunk pleaded.

"No!" she yelled.

"Please!!" he begged.

"NO!" she yelled again.

Just then, a Latina woman with long dark hair, beautiful eyes, and a calm presence, whom I can only describe as an angel sent from God, appeared behind the counter. I don't know where she came from because I was hyperventilating and about to faint.

"I am the supervisor." The patients in the waiting

room gasped.

"May I ask what the problem is?"

"This nice lady needs her scans." He put his arm on my shoulder.

The angel took my arm and gently pulled me aside.

"Look...I am very sorry about all this. We are short staffed today." She was so sweet. "If you don't mind taking a seat for just a minute, I'll get them for you. Would you like some water? I can call a nurse. *Do you need a tranquilizer?*"

"No, thank you. I'll be fine as soon as I get the results." I collapsed into a nearby chair. The tranquilizer was a tempting thought at this point, and I would have taken it if not for the long drive home.

The angel disappeared. Hunk came over and sat with me. Then I discreetly looked at him and winked, and he turned his head so others could not see him laughing.

Within minutes she returned, scans in hand, handed them to me, profusely apologizing again. The monster sniveled.

Hunk winked at me and whispered, "Good luck tomorrow."

"Thank you." I was grateful for this stranger's support. I gave him a hug. If I weren't married I would have given him my phone number too.

I walked out on a cloud, proud of standing up for myself, and it felt great! Furthermore, I had just learned how important standing up for myself would be in this fight. But mostly, I felt gratitude to the Hunk, the angel of a nurse, and Neil Simon's "Defenseless Creature."

ℛℛℛ

That night I pulled up the driveway of my home in Marin County. As I opened the door, the phone rang. I rushed inside to grab it and tripped face down over my purse, but could hear that it was my good friend Sheryl.

"Hold on," I hollered as I got back on my feet.

"Did you get it?"

"I had to pull a 'Defenseless Creature.' But I got it!" I told her as she roared with laughter.

She had played that very role for me several years earlier, as had the late Don Rickles' incredibly hilarious daughter long ago at Beverly Hills High. Sheryl and I had met through our children's schools in Marin County and became fast friends, partly because we appreciated each other's humor. She was one of the wonderful people, along with many others, who helped me with all the plays I directed for the kids. Through every performance that I directed her in, her Carol Burnett/Lucille Ball rubber-faced antics kept every audience in stitches. She is one of the funniest people I know, and steals every show. The two of us had become sort of a celebrity duo in our community. If love doesn't make the world go round, certainly laughter does.

"Good for you! I'm proud of you! It works every time."
She laughed again. "What does it say?"

"I haven't had a chance to look at it. Hold on. I have
to find my reading glasses."

After dashing frantically around the house, I finally
found them sitting on the top of my head.

"Got 'em." Squinting, I saw that several words had
been circled.

"Uptake…"

"Uptake? What the heck's uptake?" Sheryl said putting
on an exaggerated rural accent that always makes me
laugh. "It sounds like puke."

"Hell if I know." I kept reading. "I haven't learned how
to interpret a PET scan yet."

"Well, why the hell not? Have you heard from that
Dr. Neurosis yet, or Ron?"

"Neurosis said he would call as soon as he got the
report, and Ron is in Europe."

"Well, what else does the darn thing say?"

"More uptake," I snapped. Then something caught my
breath, and I paused.

"What? Why did you stop? What does it say?"

The next word jumped off the page at me. Reading
and then rereading it, the word stuck in my throat. It
took several seconds for me to comprehend the gravity
of it. It wasn't just a sick sense anymore. It was real.
Finally, its meaning was crystal clear.

"Metastasis."

"I'll be right over." She hung up. I hadn't even asked her; what a friend. I had always appreciated her friendship and adored her, but never as much as at that moment. There was no hesitation. She dropped everything to be at my side.

I was devastated, but at least I wasn't going to be alone. I went to the computer trying to find the meaning of the word "uptake," and found that it meant enhancement of probable cancer.

The phone rang again. This time it was Dr. Neurosis.

"Did you get the report, Nancy?" he asked.

"Yes...so it has already...spread?"

"Yes, I will cancel tomorrow's surgery."

"So...how long do I have?" I could barely get the words out as my voice trailed off. I wanted to hang up the phone and run, and surely didn't want to hear the answer. There was a long pause before he responded.

"Eighteen months more or less," he said without so much as an *I'm sorry, I wish had better news*.

My stomach turned upside down and I needed to vomit.

"I'll pick up my medical records tomorrow," I said.

"Very well." He hesitated, and then added sheepishly, "May I ask how you knew?"

"My father told me," I replied.

"Your father's a doctor?"

"No. He's been dead for sixteen years."

"I don't understand," he said.

"No, you don't," I said, and hung up. I did not wish to share the real story about my father's struggle with this treacherous disease, and that I had sensed my father's presence since the moment I received my diagnosis. Deep inside I already knew.

By now it was dark outside, eerily silent inside. My husband, Richard, was away on business and our daughter was spending the night at our neighbor's, so I could deal with my urgent health issues alone. Our son, Jake, was starting school in Boston.

I opened the sliding glass door to let some air in and walked out into the night. Our house sat on San Francisco Bay. There was always loud clanking of the rigging on the boats at night when the wind picked up, and it was chilly and lonely. Balmy nights are rare in Northern California; nevertheless, I kicked off my flip-flops and sat on the dock, letting my feet hang in the frigid water until I could no longer feel them. I allowed the cool numbness to spread throughout my entire body. The numbness felt like a much-needed drug on this stressful evening, and it made me feel calmer.

It reminded me how much I love the water. I can't help it. I'm a Pisces. But sometimes looking into the deep dark water reveals a scary uncertainty that comes when you can't see the bottom. It frightened me a little, like it had scared Natalie Wood, who fueled my love of acting when I was young.

Having grown up in L.A., I'm partial to swimming pools. My idea of nirvana is floating on a raft with the sun streaming down. The therapeutic relaxation of the pool had gotten me through previous stresses. I dreamed endlessly about the sunny yard and pool we had in L.A. and the many ideal days lounging around it with family and friends. Nothing was more relaxing, except the beach, which had always been another Piscean nirvana for me.

ℜ ℜ ℜ

I recalled the fun I'd had with an old boyfriend, Jeff, among other friends from my college days. Jeff and I routinely raced up Ventura Highway to that very song of the same name, to spend the weekend camping in the sand dunes at Pismo Beach, building a fire in the sand at night. In the morning everything was drenched from the dense fog: sleeping bags, clothes, towels, everything. We played Frisbee in the water and walked along the beach.

One day, Jeff, always a bit of a daredevil, thought it would be fun to drive his car on the sand, playing chicken with the waves. I told him I didn't think it was a good idea, but he insisted. Men are like that in my experience, always so stubborn. After about 10 minutes, and as predicted, the car got stuck in the water. He freaked, as his car was brand new. He jumped out of the car and, as

NANCY F. RADIN   MY BIG C

he went to get help, he yelled to me.

"Stay with the car."

I don't know why in the world I listened to him, as it was not sound advice. So, like a total idiot, I sat in the car watching the water as it rose all the way up to the windows. By that time, I realized I needed to get out of the car ASAP. Fortunately, it had a nonelectric sunroof with a hand crank, and I opened it. Squeezing through the small sunroof, I jumped off the roof of the car and waded in waist-deep water back to the shore.

By the time Jeff got back, the car was almost completely submerged in the water and needed to be towed out of the ocean. I was fine, but his ego took a beating, as the car was a total loss. We rented a car to get back home, but laughed about that for years. Even that was fun at the beach, and I felt more than ever I needed that peace to heal.

⚥ ⚥ ⚥

I was now disappointed and angry with my body for failing me. It didn't make sense, but the thought crossed my mind that my body had betrayed me. I had always taken such great care it. I had been athletic all my life: biking, skiing, running, tennis, softball, basketball, camping. You name the sport—I loved it. I had also been a vegetarian since my teens, decades before most people even knew what the word meant. "You're a veterinarian?" they would ask cluelessly.

I was always a health nut, so this came as a cruel irony. As I sat on the dock of the Bay, the Otis Redding song popped into my brain. I'd never made the connection to the song that Redding wrote on the San Francisco Bay and where I had lived before, but I began to sing to myself.

> *"Sittin' on the dock of the bay*
> *Watchin' the tide roll away*
> *Sittin' on the dock of the bay*
> *Wastin' time..."*

When I got to those two words, "wastin' time," I stopped. My fingers clutched into a fist. I had a sudden revelation: *"I don't have time to waste."* I began to panic. A strange thought came to me, "I will never have time to waste again." *More importantly, I needed a survival plan. There was absolutely no time to spare. Ever again!*

I quickly pulled my feet out of the water, and a gross, slimy piece of seaweed hung to them, which I shook off with disgust.

I tried to get Otis's song out of my head. The trouble is that can be like telling yourself *Don't think about pink elephants*—and then that's all you can think about. I had to replace that song with something uplifting *before* I was swallowed into the dark water by despair. I realized I had to summon up the power to change the soundtrack playing in my mind, the very music of my life.

I went back into the house and desperately started

thumbing through my massive music collection. A new determination rose in me. After several minutes, I found it and smiled. It was the perfect song to fill my soul with hope.

I had taken disco lessons in 1979-80 with my wonderful friend and neighbor, "Disco Dave." God knows how many times we practiced our snappy moves and turns to this song. Through her *glorious* music she gave my entire generation of women the courage to persevere through life's difficulties and triumph over them. I cranked up the speakers as the disco beat pumped, and the house shook.

Bum...bum...bum...bum...

My body began to thaw, pulsating with life. I took a breath and danced. Her name was Gloria Gaynor, and the song was "I Will Survive!"

> *"I've got all my life to live...*
> *I've got all my love to give...*
> *And I'll survive...*
> *I will survive...*
> *Hey-hey..."*

2

Mission Impossible

After the fiasco with Doctor Neurosis, it became obvious to me that if I wanted to survive—if it was even *possible* to survive—it was my responsibility to find the best possible care and to become my own advocate. I truly had to be a director, as I had been in the theatre world for decades. So why couldn't I direct the story of my own life, even my own death, if that was in my life's script?

My urgent mission now was to get other medical opinions from the top medical centers that specialized in cancer. So I did. With scans, reports, and biopsy slides in hand, I traveled around the county to three of the top cancer hospitals. I was a woman on fire, with an impossible mission, determined not to be subservient when it came to my living or dying.

My favorite center, coincidentally, was the Revlon Multidisciplinary program at UCLA, where I graduated. As a high school and college kid in L.A. back in the '60s and '70s, no place was more fun than Westwood. I studied there, lived there, worked there, and I was very familiar with the medical center. I found it to be the most compassionate and efficient of the hospitals I visited. The wonderful people there were able to expedite an appointment only three days away. They had a terrific "tumor board" program, which contained all of the needed specialists to provide evaluations and recommendations in one afternoon, as opposed to weeks or months. These included an oncologist, a radiation oncologist, an oncology surgeon, and a therapist.

In particular, I adored and was impressed with the oncologist, Dr. Linnea Chap, beautiful and brilliant in every way. I vividly recall her sitting with me late into the evening, after all the other very kind doctors had spoken individually with me and left. She remained by my side despite the fact that she had a husband and houseful of children, including newborn twins, waiting for her at home. She seemed to genuinely care about me.

Perhaps her gentle bedside manner came from being a mom. She could relate to my panic, and offered a glimmer of hope by reinforcing that cancer had not spread to my vital organs...yet. That was the only truly good bit of information, *but* it was the most important information I received. I desperately hung onto it. I had great confidence in her, and she gave me encouragement to fight. She recommended the treatments I should start with, and she said it with more kindness than I could have hoped for.

"So we can extend your life as long as possible," she affirmed. Her kindness gave me real courage and determination that I hadn't received from anyone else.

I wanted to stay in Los Angeles and have Dr. Chap treat me, but my daughter was still in high school, and I couldn't put her through a move on top of everything else. So I found another top-notch young male doctor in San Francisco through some friends I'd met in a wonderful Children's Theatre organization. His name was Dr. Grant.

His office was atop a beautiful building near the San Francisco waterfront. The first thing I noticed was a painting on his wall that stopped me dead in my tracks. Nine faceless women with identically shaped bodies but different colored body parts stood out against a bright orange background. The most significant differences in the women were their breasts or lack thereof. Several had simple horizontal slashes where their breasts no longer were. Others had diagonal slashes implying lumpectomies, some without nipples, and so on. Each woman's body told a painfully different story. The painting was breathtaking, and its impact on me at that moment was profound. Most remarkable of all to me was the signature. It had been painted by Dr. Grant himself.

I sat in his office in my thin paper-blue exam robe, which was completely uncontrollable. The matching plastic blue tie was not cooperating either, so it fell to the floor. My paper gown was open, but now I was so exhausted from the cancer ordeal, I didn't care. I was more concerned about getting my behind unstuck from the paper that covered the exam table, but couldn't get off the table to pick it up. I had always been a modest person, but because of the recent and endless probing, tests, and scans I had undergone, all modesty had disappeared. I gave up on that too, and looked up to see my medical chart, which I started reading absent any magazines within arm's reach.

I noticed four happy faces drawn on the front of my chart and had to laugh. He had a sense of humor. I liked him already. His happy faces reminded me of the tricks I resorted to when I taught "Dramatic Literature." To loosen up my senior students' resistance, I often drew cartoon stick figures of characters such as Oedipus on my handouts. They always laughed about my silly drawings at the beginning of the school year, but by final exams, believe me, I saw them in the hallways on the floor, cramming in groups by studying their cartoons.

The door opened, and the doctor walked in. I tried to close my open robe with one hand.

"Oops. I'll give you another moment," he said when he noticed I wasn't fully covered.

"It's okay. I'm not modest anymore."

He came in and pulled his chair close to me.

"Nice to meet you, Nancy." He took my other hand.

"I'm so sorry for the ordeal you have been through." He was kind as he said it, which was a welcome relief.

"We need to talk about your scans. I know you know that the cancer has already metastasized, which makes it incurable. But the good thing is it hasn't hit any of your vital organs...yet."

"Bingo!" This was the second time I'd heard that qualifying "yet" and it was welcome news—again. His kind and heartening news made me feel safe here.

He continued, "We just don't have the answers now, but hopefully, we will have them in your lifetime."

We went on to discuss the need to focus on "Palliative Treatment," which is not designed to cure the incurable, but rather to treat pain and symptoms. He suggested that I start with hormone therapy and use chemos, other drugs, and radiation as necessary, all as Dr. Chap had also suggested.

"My goal is to give you the best 'quality of life.'"

"Quality of life?" I liked the sound of that. "What exactly does it mean?" I asked.

"It means fighting the disease without destroying your ability to enjoy the rest your life, however long that will be."

I felt comfortable with that proviso, and I decided that "quality of life" would become my new mantra.

I had already decided that I would "Throw it all up on the ceiling and see what sticks!" I would try anything and everything that wouldn't make me worse—Eastern, Western, and out-of-the-box therapies.

"Do you have any questions?" he asked.

"Just one," I said

"What's that?"

"What are the happy faces for?" I needed to know that important bit of information. I figured it was code for something.

"Treatment options. They keep me pumped!" I laughed, and he smiled back at me.

"Good, let's get started." He escorted me to the chemo room.

"Make yourself comfortable, and I'll be back soon."

Over the course of my treatment, I genuinely liked him, and often thought about Dr. Chap, as well as my longtime internist, Dr. Catharine Clark-Sayles. I was tremendously fortunate to have these three outstanding doctors and people on my team. Through the serendipitous discovery of these three compassionate doctors, I learned something truly important. *When you find a great doctor, never let them go! They are truly Superheroes!*

This was all good, but one thing truly bothered me, and it was all the people I had seen in the various treatment facilities who had family members with them.

I envied them. I wasn't exactly certain how I was supposed to deal with all of this alone. Richard was away traveling most of the time, and the kids were ensconced in school. I tried not to dwell on it because it would bring me down and I couldn't afford to be any more depressed or despondent. Nor could I indulge in self-pity or in the fantasy of having other close family physically nearby to support me.

I needed to be strong if I wanted to live. So I shut out the loneliness and pretended as much as possible that it didn't exist and instead, for the moment, I tried to focus on the beauty that bloomed all around me. There I might find the solace I longed for, and the hope I needed.

Gazing out the window, I noticed a massive cruise ship docked on the Embarcadero. Despite knowing I needed to stay and fight, another part of me longed to hop on the ship and run away—but I knew I couldn't. I needed to stick around so I could challenge everything that was happening to me. I understood that I alone had to be the one in charge, because it was my life, and ultimately my responsibility.

As I looked around the room, I noticed once again my doctor's amazing artwork on the walls, listened more closely to the peaceful music playing, and appreciated the handmade blankets that created an unusually serene environment. The chemo room contained cushy loungers. I didn't know much about the concept of "feng shui," the ancient Chinese system of harmonizing with one's surroundings, but the idea of arranging myself in the right seat, at the right angle, with the most positive view certainly couldn't hurt. It was a womblike atmosphere, and it worked with me. After all the chaos and the anxiety, I began to relax.

With a few more minutes to wait, I walked around the room and began to wonder about the spirituality of each chair, as well as the health history of each of the people who had previously occupied each chair. I tried to feel the vibes or life force coming from each of them.

Like Goldilocks, I tested each chair, trying to get in touch with how I felt sitting in it. I took note of the views of the city from each one before making my decision. Despite feeling like a child playing musical chairs, I finally chose a chair that was *comfortable* and had good "vibes," as well as a lovely view of the city. In a strange way it felt as if the chair had picked me.

I was noticing the life around me with more care than ever. All this stuff is important when you're fighting for your life.

For now, I was quite happy to sit back, put my feet up, and chill. I closed my eyes, taking my emotional temperature. I wasn't aware of being unusually nervous or afraid, even though I had no idea how my body would react to the massive amounts of poison it was about to ingest.

Dr. Grant reappeared, and enthusiastically plopped himself onto a wheeled stool across the room. With one push of his legs, he propelled the stool, which marvelously stopped right in front of me.

"You're quick on that stool. Skier?" I asked.

"Yep." Taking inventory of the situation, he said, "Oops, I forgot something. Back in a flash."

Once again, he zoomed across the room and back again in the blink of an eye. This time, he returned with a pile of tubes, tape, and two clear plastic bags of liquid on his lap, which he placed on the small table next to me.

"Boy, you are fast," I said.

"I've had a lot of practice." He smiled. "Let me check your arms." His hands grazed over my arms searching for the best vein.

"Are you the only guy in town who gives his own infusions?" I asked.

"Most docs don't like to touch their own meds," he said.

"Here's a good vein. One, two, three..."

"Wait!" I panicked. "I HATE needles! I mean I really, really HATE them!"

"Trust me," he said. There was something about the way he said the word "trust," and I did.

He placed the long tubing and plastic bags just so on the I.V. stand. When everything was detangled properly, he carefully opened the valve, which allowed the liquid poison to slowly start dripping.

"Relax, and I'll be back in a bit to check on you again."
Smiling, he left me to attend to another patient who was
also receiving chemo, a fragile older woman who was
wearing a hat to hide her bald head. I smiled at her.

I took a few deep-cleansing breaths, and as I exhaled
I tried to let go of any stress or tension I was holding
onto. I knew how important it was to be receptive to
any treatment. I did so until Dr. Grant suddenly returned
five minutes later on his little stool.

He took a breath to center himself and, looking into
my eyes, he said clearly and honestly, "Studies show that
patients do better overall with their chemo when they
learn how to visualize it in a positive manner."

It made perfect sense to me. I had started practicing
transcendental meditation when I was in high school,
long before it was fashionable. I had also taught
relaxation exercises and proper breathing that is
fundamental for actors, techniques I had learned in
London while studying acting. As far as the imaging
was concerned, I was in my "wheelhouse" so to speak.
I knew the routine.

Coaxing me in a gentle voice, he said, "Now lie back
and think of the one thing that you find most relaxing,
and let it make you well."

That was the easiest part and the best offer I'd had
in a long time. As I lay back in the chair, I watched
the drips for a while. I contemplated how they formed,

the exact timing of one drip to the next, and the eventual plop—one after another after another. It was mesmerizing.

The doctor also gave me an anti-nausea medication, so I wouldn't get nauseous from the treatment. I allowed myself to welcome and accept this treatment without any struggle. I desperately wanted all of this to work. I *needed* the treatments to work for me, but mostly for my kids. For that to happen, I knew I had to completely surrender to the process.

Eventually, I closed my eyes, overcome by exhaustion. I had been unaware of the toll, the heavy burden I'd been carrying for what felt like a long time, had taken on me. I took a deep and precious breath and let it out. I imagined each drip…drip…drip sliding gleefully, splashing its way through the long tube round and round as if on a huge water slide, making its way into my vein and through my body. Finally, I came whooshing out of the tube onto a raft in my beautiful swimming pool, the one I had in L.A. I was floating with the sun streaming down on me. Everything was quiet. I completely surrendered. I would heal. I would be well.

I sat there for several hours, not thinking of anything else but floating on the raft in my pool, and allowing the cleansing of the pool to replace the poison running through my blood.

I recognized that life had dealt me a completely new set of cards. However, I just endured the first of countless treatments, and many more lay ahead. That didn't bother me. I was exactly where I needed to be.

𝓡 𝓡 𝓡

Several months later, in the spring of 2003, I was struck by more grief, which added to the weight of my health issues. My mother was dying in Los Angeles. I had been charged with her care for some years. I tried very hard to get my mother to move close to me up north, but she had a problem for every solution I offered. Older people need familiar surroundings, which I understand. Nothing I could say would convince her, which made me feel racked with guilt and sorrow.

I left for Los Angeles to be with her, making up excuses to go home every two weeks for chemo treatment and then back to be with her again. I led the secret life of a dying woman for the next five months.

As an artist, I knew Mom would appreciate having beautiful things to look at. I filled her room with balloons and lava lamps. I rearranged her bed every few days so she would have a different perspective out the window.

One day her mind wasn't there, and the next day when it was, she asked why there weren't any birds outside. I hadn't noticed but, ironically, she had. I snuck out in the yard and starting running around flapping my arms like a bird. She saw me through the window and laughed. And so did the neighbors who, unbeknownst to me, were watching the entire time.

MISSION IMPOSSIBLE

I also put all the family photos in a slideshow on my laptop, which I laid on her tummy so she could look back at her life and see the family she created and loved so very much.

That afternoon, I turned on the TV and was delighted at the serendipitous sight of Robin Williams in a Francis Coppola film, *Jack,* which my daughter had acted in as a young child.

It reminded me of when my dear friend Vicky and I had schlepped my mom around in her wheelchair to every theatre in the Woodland Hills Multiplex just to catch the trailer of that movie over and over again, which my daughter was also featured in.

My mom and I watched the entire movie on this day. Every time Dina appeared we cheered. Seeing her granddaughter in that major Hollywood movie was wonderful, and the last thing Mom ever watched.

We had adored her, though she could drive us crazy at times. I strived to show my mother in her final months that, despite the personal suffering she endured throughout her life, she had triumphed and accomplished a great deal through her laughter and love of family. She was like her father, the "Miracle Man."

It had been a relatively peaceful time for my mother, who had no idea of the state of chaos my life was in, and I was grateful for that. caring for her at the end of her life brought me great peace and I will always treasure that time with her. But the truth was that I am glad she

35

never knew that I was serioussly ill. She was suffering enough and I cannot imagine the pain it would have caused her. I did my best to never let on that things were awry with my health or my life. Mothers have an undeniable sixth sense about their children. The day she was beginning to slip away, she asked, "Are you happy, sweetheart?"

I lied and I told her I was. I truly hoped she believed me.

3

Shock

A few days after my mother passed away, I made a quick trip home to S.F. for chemo treatment, and returned immediately to L.A., staying at my brother's for the terrible ritual of sorting through my mom's things. A week of sad nostalgia exhausted me and made me anxious. I couldn't wait until I got home again. I desperately needed some loving support and rest.

The night before my final flight back to the Bay Area, I collapsed in bed and was on the verge of sleep around 10 p.m. when I heard some familiar and eerie music:

What was that?

It started to play again.

And then again, It reminded me of something from Rod Serling's *The Twilight Zone.*

I sat up disoriented and looked around. The TV wasn't turned on. Hmmm. I noticed my cell phone vibrating

around on the nightstand and was about to do a pirou-
ette onto the floor. It took a few minutes until I could
figure out where the music was coming from. Then I
remembered that after my mom's funeral, my son told
me he had put a new ringtone on my phone. He said it
was in case Grandma wanted to call us. As always, he
made me laugh.

"Hello?"

"It's me. Guess where I am?" Richard said with the
enthusiasm of a kid at Disneyland. "Guess where I'm
going now? Swit..." My heart sank with disappointment.
After a long pause, I asked, "You're not coming home?"

"No. I need a break," he said matter-of-factly.

I was more disoriented than ever. Nothing was making
sense. I couldn't possibly have heard him correctly.

"*You* need a break? You're joking, right?" I repeated
the words I thought he had uttered.

"No, it's been a really hard time for me and I need a
break," he reiterated.

"For *you?*" I was utterly flabbergasted. Was this the
same man I had lived with for a quarter of a century?
Apparently not. I wanted to reach through the phone
and strangle him. I simply couldn't tolerate his insen-
sitivity to my needs at this critical time. I would never
do something like this to him in a million years. My head
was spinning. I was speechless. I had no idea what to say
next. I was beyond devastated, but it was clear to me

that a decision needed to be made, although it was not mine to make. It was his decision, and his alone. He either cared or he didn't, and it was well beyond my control. I had no choice in the matter.

After a few moments, I began to speak slowly and deliberately, "Listen to me." I took a breath and then took the biggest gamble of my life.

"Are you listening, Dick?" I repeated.

"Yes, I'm listening."

"Either you come home now...or don't come home at all."

After all these years, as horrible as it was, I had just given him an ultimatum.

"Fine," he said, and hung up. He was oblivious. That was it.

"*Fine*" *what?* I was paralyzed. I had no idea what "fine" meant.

Did he mean, "Fine, I'm coming home?" Or, "Fine, I'm not."

Was he buying time to think about it? What was there to think about? I was his wife, who had just been through two major traumas, and we had two children together. He wasn't offering to take me on a restful vacation, not that I even had the strength to take one right now. And, if he needed time to think about it, what did that say about our relationship, which could only mean one thing—it was over, just like that.

41

Too tired to worry or cry, I fell back into bed. I felt so disgusted. Any thoughts that he might have a change of heart, well, I would just have to wait and see. I threw the phone on the floor and pulled the covers over my head. It was dark, but this darkness felt safer than daylight when life becomes very real. There was nothing I could do about any of it right now. I don't think I even told my brother.

When I couldn't fall asleep after several hours, I got up, took my blanket out to the yard, and sat by the swimming pool. The beautiful blue light reflected in the pool and the stillness of the night calmed me down. I stayed for quite a while, hoping that morning would be a long way off, and eventually fell asleep outside.

But it wasn't a long way off, and when I returned home to Marin the following day, Dick wasn't at home—and I had my answer. I clearly knew what "fine" meant. I was shattered to the core that anyone would do this to me, let alone my husband.

I was terribly worried, mostly for my daughter, Dina, who was sixteen, and I understood that this was the worst possible time for her. Jake, seventeen, was starting college in Boston, which had been planned before I got sick.

𖤐 𖤐 𖤐

Over the next months, I did my best to reconcile the

marriage, for Dina's sake more than mine. After much marital negotiation we struck a kind of reconciliation, and eventually he moved back in. But the bond of trust was shattered beyond repair. He had one foot in the door and one foot out. We were about to celebrate our twenty-fifth anniversary, although I had known him since he moved here from Europe, when I was only nineteen and attending UCLA.

I felt emotionally and physically ambushed, and was back in the hospital now on a clinical trial drug that was later discontinued for causing too many fatalities. It was as if my body had become a human science experiment.

While I was waiting to be discharged in the morning and wondering if my husband would be there to accompany me home, the nurse came into my room.

"Your husband is stuck in New York on business."

"Seriously?" I said.

"I think he's using this time to..." Her voice trailed off as "Code Blue" was announced over the intercom.

"What? He's what?" I needed to know.

"Never mind," she said, and left the room to respond to the urgent page. What *didn't* she tell me? I was obsessing and rapidly becoming distraught.

I found out later in the day that he wanted a divorce, and there I was, utterly and completely alone. My hands were shaking and my eyes welled with tears. I was having trouble catching my breath, and I was afraid I was going to black out, pass out from the stress. I had spent practically my entire life in servitude to others—family, friends, community, students, and even strangers—and there I was, completely alone.

At that very moment, a man entered the room, but he clearly wasn't a doctor. He was dressed all in black. "Are you okay?" he asked.

"I think I'm having a panic attack." This was a really fun and new idiosyncrasy since my diagnosis.

"Can I get you something?"

"Please just stay for a moment," I said softly, pleading like a frightened little child.

"I'm the hospital chaplain, Bruce, and I've been meaning to come and see you this week. But they've had you out of your room a lot to run tests on you. I understand you've been through quite an ordeal. Would you like to talk? I'm a good listener."

His timing was spooky. God had clearly sent him here to comfort me. To be honest, I didn't care if he was a priest, a monk, or a voodoo witch doctor, I needed his help.

"I have to tell you I am Jewish in a cultural way, a Reform Jew," I said. I had never reached out to a rabbi before.

"That's good, because I'm a rabbi."

"Wow!" With that amazing clarification, he smiled kindly and pulled out his yarmulke, which he gently kissed and gracefully put on his head.

"Did they send you in here just now?" I asked skeptically.

"No, why?"

"Your timing is amazing! Actually, I am really flabbergasted. I'm feeling very much alone."

"May I say a prayer for you?" The kindness in his voice touched me.

"I'll take anything you have, thank you." I smiled. I wasn't big on praying in large congregations, but personal prayer had always been important to me. If ever there was a time for me to pray, it was now. I was verging on desperation.

The rabbi pulled out two Shabbat candles from a little black velvet bag. I had not realized it was Friday and although it was not yet sundown, we lit them and said the prayer. Then, he took my hand.

"I'd like to sing the blessing for healing," he said with a profound sense of caring. We both closed our eyes and he sang it to me.

I was deeply moved in a way I never had been before by any clergy and my eyes moistened with tears. More than anything, I felt that God was somehow watching over me, and was telling me that this was all happening to me for a reason. I needed to hold onto that thought to get through it, although I would have to figure out why later on. After a few more moments of silence, I thanked him from the bottom of my heart. Then he disappeared through the door as quickly as he had slipped in.

Still struck by his timing, I felt it was one of the most serendipitous experiences I'd ever had. Despite my sense of panic, I took the rabbi as a sign which renewed my strength, and which allowed me to get myself home.

4

Life Elevated

I was thrilled to finally leave the claustrophobic conditions of my hospital room. Any room without fresh air or sunshine makes me feel suffocated. I've always needed windows that open to let in the air and life from outside.

However and according to hospital regulations, I had to be escorted to the downstairs in a wheelchair. The attendant was a nice young Filipino fellow who reminded me of the wonderful Filipina woman who had helped take care of my mother in her last months. Maria was such a warm and wonderful person, as was this young man pushing me.

We entered the elevator, and as the doors nearly closed two goofy teenaged brothers shoved their skateboards between the doors, which automatically reopened them so the boys could enter. They were laughing hysterically about photos they'd apparently taken.

"Whoa, this one's weird. Look at his eyes, Grandpa looks like he's already dead." They laughed. I thought their laughter was refreshing, and it actually cheered me up. The attendant was not amused, however, and shot the older, taller-looking brother a look of disapproval.

"Hey, man," the taller one said to the shorter one, "not now." When he noticed me he became awkward and mumbled, "Sorry, ma'am."

"It's okay. I'm sure you boys love your grandfather, and you are just worried. I think laughing sometimes helps."

"Yeah, exactly!" said the older one, as if I was the only one on the planet who got it.

From the decade that I taught as a drama teacher at Beverly Hills High School, I recognized he was a sensitive and intelligent kid who probably often got in trouble for acting out in immature ways, but without malice.

Watching their shenanigans, my mind traveled back to my own youth as a kid in Chicago. I practically grew up in hospital waiting rooms, babysitting my younger brother.

I thought about my grandfather, Marvin, who required two crude wooden legs from diabetes spun out of control. First one leg, and then months later the other, needed to be amputated. Just the initial thought of it made me sick, and I was afraid. But, throughout the ordeal he never showed an ounce of self-pity, and I'm convinced that my memory of his courage made a difference when I descended into the fight for my own life.

※ ※ ※

It was the early 1960s, and believe me, they were no "blade runners." Back then, children were never allowed upstairs to visit with patients, but every now and then my dad would sneak us up under his long coat. The nurses knew, but pretended not to see. They adored and admired my grandpa for his courage and determination, and knew it was good medicine for him to get a visit from his grandkids. All the nurses and doctors at the hospital called him the "Miracle Man."

When he came home, after almost a year, he stayed with us for a time, although it was terribly difficult on his strong sense of independence to rely on others. My dad and uncle would lift him into a tub and bathe him several times a week.

I considered it a privilege that he allowed me to help him strap his wooden legs on in the morning, and help him take them off at night. His trust me made me feel so special, and I'd set them to the side of his bed.

"Don't step on my toes," he liked to joke, which always made me giggle.

I would lie on the other bed and we would do bicycle exercises together. His stumpy little legs going round and round in circles made us laugh. His laughter reminded him that, despite his difficulty, he was still alive and would not let the loss of his legs define him. And, to his great credit, I was never afraid of those wooden legs, as many children would be.

Afterward, I would place a glass of water on the nightstand.

"Goodnight, honey. I love you. Oh, would you leave the hall light on?"

"And the door open," I replied softly. "I know, Grandpa. I love you too,"

It gave him security knowing we were nearby and all he had to do was holler. Nighttime in bed, without his legs, was the only time I ever saw him a little scared.

He made it his mission in life to relearn how to walk so that he could dance at his grandson's wedding the following year. I'll be damned if he didn't. I vividly remember the dashing image of him in his tuxedo and white hair, struggling to stand up at the table and to hold onto my grandma for support. It wasn't so much dancing as it was rocking back forth on the dance floor, but his mission was certainly accomplished.

I couldn't possibly have imagined back then, as a young child, how the strength and courage that I saw in him would inspire me throughout my life. His improbably positive attitude had been duly noted in my child's soul, and was where I learned to deal with pain

and loss through a lightness of spirit, and humor—
sometimes dark, sometimes light, and sometimes both
at the same time.

※ ※ ※

When the elevator got to the ground floor, the two boys
bolted out and immediately resumed laughing at the
photos of their grandpa. The attendant apologized for
their behavior. To me, laughter was a necessary part of
visiting people in the hospital. How else does one cope?
Laughter can be a lifeline.

Their laughter triggered another memory.

"Nancella," as my cousin Dan calls me. "Hold the
elevator! We're coming." I was transported to when I
was around thirty.

※ ※ ※

The automatic elevator door was stopped from closing
this time by a tennis racket jutted between the doors.
First to enter was my cousin, Dan, fresh off the court
in his white tennis attire. One after the other, ten family
members crammed their way into the cramped elevator
like clowns in a VW. The other ten took the adjacent
elevator.

This protracted hospital experience was a bizarre time
when both my dad and my uncle (brothers-in-law) suffered

sudden heart attacks and surgery by the same doctor, on the very same day, and both in a Santa Monica hospital.

It was 6 p.m. and the aroma of fresh corned beef and dill pickles wafted through the elevator. The illicit food was concealed under our mothers' Hawaiian muumuus, which were poolside fashion of the day for many housewives in Los Angeles.

My eldest cousin, Ron, the doctor, reprimanded our moms. "I told you you're not supposed to bring that food here!"

"The nurses will never know," my aunt Beverly said. I absolutely adored her and she was a second mom to me.

"They asked for it," my mom confirmed.

"That cholesterol-ridden food is why they're both in the hospital in the first place!"

My aunt and mom were the funniest sister comedy duo I've ever known. They lovingly made funny faces to the rest of us when Ron turned his back to them. Ron was the smartest one in our family, and we all revered him.

Both elevators arrived on the fourth floor at the same time, and all twenty of us exited the elevators. Half of us went to be with my uncle, and the other half went to my dad's room. This had become our daily 6 p.m. ritual.

The hospital decided to put them next door to each other at the end of the hallway for our family's sake, but probably more so for the hospital's sake—and to keep all the commotion and the contraband deli smells confined to a remote area.

My dad, who was the sweetest and most gentle man I've ever known, was also the strongest and most robust man I've ever known. In fact, he taught hand to hand combat in World War II, and fought at Normandy. I never got used to seeing him weak or frail. Somehow he managed to remain upbeat, which I found amazingly inspirational.

I had particular fun with my uncle, however. I would sit in the chair at the foot of his bed. He forgot that he was connected to a heart monitor, which was hung directly over his head and which he could not see.

"I'm not going to worry about money anymore, and I am not going to let Beverly irritate me from here on out." He repeated that several times.

Every time he said "money" and "Beverly" the heart monitor spiked hilariously out of control. It was like a lie detector test...heehee. I loved to tease him about that. It was another lesson in laughing through the pain, using humor to transcend crisis or tragedy.

At 7 p.m., halfway through visiting hours, there was a lot of commotion as we all switched rooms for part two of our daily family festivities. At 8 p.m., or as soon as the nurses could get rid of us, we'd all take the elevators down together, laughing about our visits.

Many of the nurses remarked that they had never seen such a devoted family. Of course, they also loved the desserts we often brought and shared with them.

All of us did that every night for six weeks. No one ever planned it. That's just the way we were. Unconditional love, now and forever.

5

On My Way Home

Alone and finally outside of the hospital from my week-long stay, I stepped into the late afternoon blast of California Indian summer heat. It was a nice change from the frigid hospital temperature that is kept that way to avoid the spread of illness. Lugging my hastily packed suitcase with one broken wheel, my body felt weak and my legs like Jell-O.

I wandered through the parking lot, already sweating, searching for my old silver BMW Z3 roadster. I was so happy to see that little car, which brought real joy to my life, in a hair-blowing-in-the-wind sort of way. I always thought of my car as a *she*, and was relieved to find she hadn't abandoned me at the hospital, but was patiently waiting for me like a loving and devoted dog.

We had given my SUV "mom car" to our daughter when she got her license earlier in the year so she could get back and forth from school, as there were no buses and it was miles away. I decided to get a little convertible like I'd always had before kids. I found this slightly used car in Santa Monica at a great price while visiting my mom in L.A. It served me well as a wonderful midlife-crisis-mobile.

I swiped my finger across the hood, thick with dust. She was stifling hot— from the beating she'd taken from the weeklong heat. I opened the windows, popped the convertible top, and dumped my suitcase, now somehow missing two wheels, on the passenger seat.

The seat and steering wheel scorched me as my skin touched them, so I grabbed the doggy towel off the car floor to sit on. Collapsing into the low-contoured seat, I started the car, revved it a couple of times, and snaked my way to the parking lot attendant's booth. The sizzling ticket was still on the dashboard where I'd left it, and I handed it to a seedy looking fella with a ponytail who had rap music blaring from the booth.

"Twenty dollars per day...that'll be...um...er...one hundred sixty dollars, lady," he said.

"Wow...but it's only been seven days, not eight."

"It's 5:07. After 5 p.m., I have to charge you another day."

I'd spent many hours packed, ready and waiting for my discharge papers. Now it was rush hour, and as I glanced in the rearview mirror, I saw a line of impatient people in cars forming behind me.

"I don't have that much cash. Will you take a credit card?"

"Sure, lady."

I handed him my card, and was then hit with a sudden wave of nausea. Reaching into the glove box, I grabbed a little doggy poop bag and held it to my mouth.

"Declined," he said.

"Huh?" I was shocked.

"Your card's been declined, lady!" I was confused and desperate to get home.

"That doesn't make any sense. Try this." I exchanged cards with him.

"Still declined," he said a moment later.

The cars started honking at me, which made me even more agitated. I was feeling sicker and sicker, and now held hostage and betrayed this time by *a machine!*

I could feel froth building in my mouth, and held the bag to my chin. I spoke like a ventriloquist, moving my mouth as little as possible so the froth wouldn't seep out.

"Can I give you a check?"

"We don't take checks, lady."

The honking grew louder as I was hit with another knee-buckling wave of nausea, and grabbed the bag again. Not able to hold it back any longer, I puked into the bag. The attendant looked at me with disgust.

"I can't let you go without paying, lady."

"Seriously? Look at me." I kind of wished I'd have puked on him.

Thankfully, the other parking attendant came to the window. Letting go with a long sigh, he said kindly, "Let her go, Joe. I got her license plate. We'll send you a bill. Feel better, ma'am."

Nodding thanks, I hit the gas and tore out of the lot, hoping to get home before I vomited again.

Two blocks away from the hospital, at the nearest intersection, I was pulled over by a policeman who had seen me driving with the bag up to my face. When he demanded my license, I showed him the hospital wristband I was still wearing instead, and my discharge papers. When he realized the gravity of the situation he was very kind.

"Can I get you something?" he asked. "There's a 7-Eleven at the corner."

Wow, what a really nice cop, I thought.

"I'll be OK in a few minutes." I could barely speak, remembering the nausea medication in my pocket, which the doctor had given "in case."

The policeman was genuinely concerned about my getting home safely. Seeing I could trust him, I showed him the fast-acting pill and popped it under my tongue to dissolve. Within several minutes, I was relieved to finally let go of the blue bag. When the officer felt it was safe for me to drive, he let me go and wished me well. I thanked him profusely.

I decided to put it all out of my mind and enjoy the beautiful drive home. I turned on the CD and blasted

Gloria's iconic song, the only one I ever played anymore, "I Will Survive."

Soon I was glancing up 746 feet at the two iconic towers of the Golden Gate Bridge. The bridge is not gold, but really more of a burnt orange or deep rust color. The misnomer is not a big deal nor does it diminish the bridge's beauty, but it was a perfect symbol for the short-sighted doctors who had misdiagnosed me, not willing to look any further than what at first glance appeared obvious to them that the cancer had not spread. They had missed what was right before their very eyes, which frustrated me to no end.

It was late by the time I got home. Our daughter was staying again with her best friend, who lived near us. It was the girls' first day of their junior year in high school, and missing school today was not an option. Jake was still in Boston.

I recognized that they needed to have their own lives, and I decided I wanted to keep them as uninvolved in my care as long as possible. I intentionally avoided asking them for assistance with medical appointments and treatments when they were around unless absolutely necessary. For that reason, right or wrong, I chose not to share with them the updated and much worse pronosis until much later. When I got home, I just fell into bed.

The next morning I woke up groggy from the insomnia that had become yet another fun issue in my restless life. I made some Italian roast, the only coffee I keep at home, and walked outside on the deck and into the sun, which always made me feel better. It was windy, so I tightened my robe. Boats were rocking all around me. I sat down on one of the white wooden Adirondack chairs I had just purchased because they were strong and very heavy. The torrential gusts that we experienced daily in our little microclimate, of the many in Marin, could not blow these into our neighbor's yard like our previous deck chairs had.

Halfway through my coffee, I suddenly remembered the problems the previous day with the credit cards. I started to choke, dropped my cup, and ran into the bedroom to throw on some clothes. I jumped in the car and raced to the bank.

When I arrived it still wasn't open, but that didn't stop me. I stood at the glass doors and banged on them like Dustin Hoffman in the final scene of *The Graduate*. The manager came over to the door. She recognized me and, sensing my panic, unlocked the doors and let me in.

Stepping inside, I became very emotional, so she summoned one of the tellers to bring me some tea. Like old friends, we sat down and talked. I recounted the events of the previous twenty-four hours, and that my credit cards were not working. She was mortified, and immediately went to investigate our bank accounts. The nice young teller who brought me tea sat with me until the manager returned. I couldn't speak.

Five or ten minutes later, the manager walked reluctantly towards me. I could tell from her worried expression that the news wasn't good. She handed me some papers and tried to remain kind and compassionate as she explained that all of our bank accounts had been emptied and closed. Nothing was left. Nada, zip, zero!

"I'm *so* sorry," she said, holding back her own tears. She kept apologizing profusely, saying that there was absolutely nothing she could have done to prevent this, nor was there anything she could now do to remedy it.

"I understand," I said quietly. My soul was crushed yet again.

She offered to personally drive me home. I thought that was sweet, and though I tried to maintain my composure, my eyes were welling up with tears. What would I do? I had no idea.

Eventually, I thanked her for her kindness and left the bank. I staggered to my car and fumbled for my keys. By the time I sat behind the wheel I was shaking. I sat there numb for a long time, too teary-eyed to drive. I reached for my phone, not even knowing whom to call. It didn't matter anyway because I had left the house in such a rush that I forgot to bring the phone with me.

Sitting in the car, I didn't even have the wherewithal to turn on the ignition. I sat there immobile, thinking about trust. I had trusted my husband. How could I not trust him? He was my husband! But trust, it dawned on me, is a double-edged sword, with betrayal being the other side of the blade. Trust is wonderful when honored, and devastating when broken. Would I ever be able to trust anyone again? I simply don't even remember driving myself home.

When I slipped into the driveway of our house in Marin, I sat there wondering how my life had become so unraveled. How could all these betrayals have seemingly come out of the blue? What happened to my life? Was there something I had or hadn't done? I had been a faithful and dedicated mom and wife who always put my family ahead of myself. I needed another struggle like I needed a hole in my head, as if what I was already facing was not battle enough.

Where was my family, which had provided so much comfort and security when I was young? They were now spread all over the country. My parents were gone, my sister and brother lived in different cities, and both kids were away. Even our two dogs were gone.

My downfall was my health, which was beyond my control. I was truly alone, utterly and completely alone, and worse, I was terrified.

When I got home, I walked right through the living room, then the kitchen, and out onto the deck. I was suffocating and needed some fresh air. The morning fog was clearing, and it was turning into a beautiful day. I was too wired to sleep. I had never been a day-napper. I hated wasting the precious daytime, and today was no different.

Gazing out over the Bay, I realized that I needed to do something to clear my head. I walked into the garage. Tucked in the very corner and under a dusty tarp was one of my most treasured possessions: my little yellow Vespa, which I hadn't ridden since my diagnosis. I was the only person in our community who had one at the time. Neighbors honked and waved continuously when I rode it out and about town. My daughter was mortified, but my son thought it was hilarious—and coveted it.

I ripped off the cover and put on my matching yellow bumblebee helmet. She started right up, and off I went. I headed to the Marin Headlands, which is on the north side of the Golden Gate, up and over hills to the aptly named Skyline Highway. I rode through miles and miles of the massive and towering redwood trees, down to the flower-filled, evergreen valley, where the Pelican Inn, a perfectly situated English pub near Muir Beach, awaited me. Every time I cross the threshold of that wonderful pub, I swear I'm back in the English country-side, especially Stratford-upon-Avon, which I vividly remember from my time spent in London in the bicen-tennial year, 1976.

This ride never fails to thrill me. It's a magnificent blend of astounding sights, sounds, and crispness in the air. It is heaven on earth. I ascend the mountain again towards the endless blue sky, and a picture perfect view of the Pacific. Sometimes whales can be seen shooting water from their holes as they surface and then bellyflop back down into the deep blue sea. It truly is God's breathtaking country. I stopped to take it all in.

Yanking off my helmet so my view wouldn't be obscured, my "helmet hair" shot straight up from the static electricity. When I turned my head slightly to the left I saw the swooping steel bridge perfectly framing the heart of the world's most beautiful city, which was shining across the Bay. Massive cargo and cruise ships, so large it boggles the mind how they stay afloat, were slipping under the bridge by what seemed inches. Tilted sailboats danced across the water.

Gazing over the Bay, I suddenly fell into a dangerous reverie. Looking hundreds of feet straight down the hillside frightened me. Out of nowhere, a strange thought attacked me, sending a frisson of fear through me: *I could end all of this suffering here and now.*

However, at that moment, of all the people in the world who could have come into my mind, it was the Austrian psychiatrist Viktor Frankl. I thought about his observation, learned during his incarceration in Auschwitz, that we can endure almost anything *if* we find meaning in the experience—even a concentration camp, even death. He expounded upon Nietzsche's concept, "He who has a *why* to live for, can bear almost any *how.*" I truly needed to find meaning in the pain that was racking my body, my mind, and my soul.

Suddenly, the stellar view of San Francisco Bay was replaced by a vision of the faces of my two children.

First, I began to tremble out of fear, and then out of love. I recalled what I never should have forgotten, that they were my purpose in life, and my love for them, as Frankl also stated, could keep me alive as long as God would allow.

I stayed for a long time, searching from this great place of magnificence for the courage and strength to go on. After my long reverie, I picked up my yellow helmet and put it back on, thinking *my life isn't over yet, but it is irrevocably changed and will never be the same—ever again.*

With a strengthened sense of resolve, I jumped back on my Vespa for the long ride back home to face whatever lay ahead.

6

Descent into
the Twilight Zone

The next phase of my life felt like a descent into many episodes of the legendary *Twilight Zone* series. It was a combination of science nonfiction and just plain craziness. What began as a series of head-thumping experiences was turning into something like PTSD, post-traumatic stress disorder, such as happens to suffering soldiers and other trauma victims. The sum total of the separation, worrying about my kids, money, cancer, and my mom's recent death were making me what I most feared becoming: neurotic.

It was also the first time in my life when I was painfully unable to have an outlet for creativity, which had always provided certain levity and another crucial meaning to my life, which Dr. Frankl talked about in his book.

Thankfully, I had a secret weapon. I was blessed with

one true constant adult I could rely on. My sister, Lara, was there for me day and night although she lived three thousand miles away. Throughout my ordeal, we talked multiple times a day, and she came to visit with me quite a bit after my husband had left.

Fortunately, I also had an amazing internist who had been my doctor for fifteen years, Dr. Catharine Clark-Sayles. She quarterbacked me through the confusing labyrinth of the medical cancer world. Her kindness and generosity of spirit have helped me through many trying times. She is also an amazing published poet. *Again, having a wonderful doctor is the most important thing when fighting serious illnesses.*

ጸ ጸ ጸ

The first day of my scheduled radiation I was especially nervous. The very presence of cancer was terrifying enough, but one of my tumors was located in an especially dangerous area on my spine, adjacent to the spinal cord and close to my heart. One slight mistake with the radiation could kill or paralyze me.

On the way to the hospital, Lara and I stopped at the pharmacy inside a nearby market to pick up some medication, which doctors routinely prescribe for relaxation for this procedure—like shampoo with conditioner. We also needed to buy a ton of candy, not for us, but to be ready for Halloween that night.

It was unseasonably warm for this time of year, so it

seemed strange seeing people in costume in the market. It reminded me of the Christmas decorations on palm trees in Los Angeles over the winter holidays, which always look incongruous. We were about to be besieged by kids, mostly teenaged trick-or-treaters who would descend upon us that evening. I grabbed a wheeled cart to lean on as my sister walked at a quick clip ahead of me.

"Slow down, please," I asked her. I was weak and exhausted and couldn't keep up with her.

"Oh my God," she said. "I'm so sorry. I keep forgetting you're sick."

That was the moment I woke up to the difficulty many people have in relating to illness. Hearing my sister's genuinely sorry voice, I realized that to most eyes, my illness was invisible, at least at this point. I still had my hair and, although I was thin, otherwise looked normal. It was the first of many lessons I was to learn about being sick. I found that if you do not visibly appear ill and, most of all, still have your hair, people tend to forget, even those closest to you. It's human nature, and certainly not malicious or anyone's fault. It just is what it is. However, her unintentional forgetfulness made me feel invisible.

On the other hand, there are some people who just love a good train wreck, "rubberneckers" I guess you'd call them.

I was dazed and not really paying attention when my shopping cart collided into someone else's.

"Sorry," I said, quickly glancing up. When I saw that it was my neighbor Sue, I quickly tried to steer my cart in the opposite direction, pretending not to notice her. Sue was the ultimate rubbernecker, an annoying gossip or "yenta," and one of those people who has absolutely no filter. I couldn't abide the thought of a long chat at that moment. I was too distraught, on edge, for small talk.

"Oh God," I thought, "please not now."

"Nancy," she said in her Southern draaaaawl. I'd been caught.

"I've been meaning to caaall you."

Thank God she hadn't. I had avoided her like the plague. Her house was only 30 feet from mine, which elevated avoidance to an art form.

"How are you coping, you poooor thing?

"Actually, it's nice to get out and not have to think about it, Sue."

"Well…you know we're all in this fight together. I mean, not in the trenches…like you."

I looked for the nearest escape route.

"Speaking of trenches. Sue, I really need to go. My sister's taking…"

"So…are those implants, or are those yours?" She was glaring at my chest.

"Huh? They're mine," I replied. Geez. This was exactly what I was trying to avoid.

"But...I thought you had a mastect—"

How the hell could she have known that? I wondered.

"No...as it turned out."

"Well, thank God for that! I just know Joe would leave if I ever lost mine...God forbid. What about radiation?"

"Today, actually."

Where the hell was my sister? I swiveled around, hoping she would save me. I was ready to explode.

"Really? Do you have any of those funny little tattoo dots?"

Clearly, escape was not an option. I figured if I told her what she wanted to know, she'd leave me alone.

"Yes, I do. Right here. I pointed to the middle of my chest.

"Oh my God! A friend of mine back home had radiation in the same spot. They blew up her aorta and she died right on the table."

"For God's sake, Sue!" My beloved aunt Beverly had actually died from a ruptured aorta. That aside, how could she say that to me right now?

"I knooow, can you believe it?" She was oblivious.

"Unbelievable," I said referring to her, but my sarcasm went waaay over her head.

"Swear to Gaaaahd!" She drew out the name of God for what seemed, ironically, like an eternity. I bit my lip.

"Well. Thanks for the pep talk, Sue, but I have to…"

"Good luck today…especially with your aorta. You caaaall me if you need anything at aaall…or just want someone to talk. I'm right across the street. Don't be a stranger. Bahyeee!"

That's never gonna happen, I thought as I turned to the frozen-food freezer and thumped my head several times against the glass door. One of the box boys, noticing my head-banging, asked if I was having trouble finding something.

"Just my life. I'm fine, thanks," I responded wearily.

"Huh?" he said, looking at me like I was totally insane, and shrugged his shoulders as he walked away.

I would talk to anyone—but Sue. I knew she was trying to be helpful, and then I wondered why it was it so hard for people to act naturally around sick people. It was as if they felt my illness or something about it was contagious.

Lara was now paying the cashier, and I went over to her.

"Please get me out of here," I said.

It was only 2 p.m., but the parking lot was very congested from people doing their last-minute Halloween shopping. As we got to the car, a pickup truck pulled up next to us. The guy in it was either wearing a cowboy costume or was a cowboy, I couldn't tell. The other strange fact was that he had antlers attached to the front hood of his truck. Now that's something you sure as shootin' don't see too many of in upscale Marin County.

"Hey...you know that's a handicap spot?"

"Yes, we have a permit, thanks," Lara said, pointing to the plaque hanging from the windshield. I did appreciate it when people said something. I had received a few tickets when I had forgotten to hang the permit.

"Neither of you looks handicapped to me! You fucking people!" he shouted. That did it! I was mad and got out of the car.

"Just forget it!" Lara yelled out of the car window, knowing my spunk.

"Hey, Buffalo Bill? May I have your address?" I yelled.

"My address? What for?" He was shocked.

"You know, some people have invisible illnesses, and I'd really like to send you my next chemo bill!" He gave me the finger, and pulled away.

I got back in the car, feeling like I had at least spoken up for myself and my fellow cancer patients. I was apoplectic with anger, and then out of nowhere came a burst of laughter.

"You can't let ignorant people like that upset you," Lara said through her own laughter.

"What's wrong with people? What's wrong with *me?*"

"You're just under a lot of stress," she said sympathetically.

"Ya think?" I laughed.

As Lara drove, all I could think of during the drive to radiation was my aorta blowing up on the table. I had to find a way of calming down.

Thank God, the radiation tech, or "Big Guy" as I called him, was a real sweetheart. He had made my body mold for the radiation (which was to keep my body from any possible movement) several days earlier. That day we'd had a nice chat for a couple hours while he was measuring me, literally, from head to toe, shaping the mold. He had tried to distract me from what he was doing by asking me about my background. I told him that I had taught theatre. He had asked me for a favor, which I was happy to oblige, having to do with planning a surprise for his kids for Halloween.

"How are you doing today, cutie?" Big Guy greeted me with a warm smile.

I handed him a couple of bags of candy I bought for the radiation team who were so wonderful, but I was disappointed that none of them were in Halloween costumes, like others around the hospital campus.

"Thanks," he said. "How sweet."

"I'm a little nervous." He gave me a hug.

"That's normal."

"How come you're not in costume?" I asked.

"Got to maintain a sober atmosphere here." He pouted.

"I'll be waiting right here. I love you," Lara said.

Thank God she was with me.

"I love you too. If I can't feel my fingers or toes when I'm done, use my advanced directive!" I laughed, but she knew I was totally serious. We had discussed quality of life and what I could and couldn't live with many times. "I love you, too!"

Big Guy then beckoned me to his office. "My costume's in here. I'll show you." His costume was on a hanger suspended from the top of the door.

"Nice costume." It was the coolest high-tech glow-in-the-dark skeleton. I gave him a high five.

"Hey, have you ever heard of aortas blowing up from radiation?"

"Nah, never heard of that." He laughed.

"Good! " I was relieved.

"That would be messy!"

We both laughed as he escorted me down the hall.

"Oh, speaking of mess…"

I pulled a little red bottle out of my pocket and handed it to him.

"Here's what I promised you."

"Wow, thanks," he said excitedly. "The kids will love the fake blood. So, ya ready?"

"I am now!"

"Good, let's do it." He gave me another high five and helped me up onto the table.

He had done a great job putting me at ease. His humor

and kindness made me feel relaxed as we began. How ironic that this place, of all places, was where I felt understood.

While feeling surprisingly at ease, an idea came to me. I decided that when I got my energy back, I would become a volunteer at a hospital. If I could help other cancer patients who were less fortunate than I had been, it would be very worthwhile. In the meantime, I needed to get through this never-ending ordeal.

After my husband left, we had to sell our house and I had to find another home. This one was much smaller, not a luxurious Marin County home on the Bay featuring a beautiful dock, but I loved it.

Later that afternoon, as soon as we got home, I quickly changed and headed to my happy place, the pool, *which really wasn't so much of pool as a big aqua-colored camping tarp.* I had laid it out perfectly over the pavement to look more like a pool than concrete, and put a few potted palm trees around the tarp. A rubber float sat on the tarp, which was at the ready for impulse floating. A large-brimmed sun hat and cup holder lay on the float too. I desperately needed the fantasy. I had asked the doctor if I could hang a chemo pole from the float, but he nixed that idea, which was disappointing.

My fantasy pool helped me with my meditation and visualization. I needed it for my soul. It was a placeholder pool until, hopefully, one day, I could move to a place with a real pool again, like the one I had had in L.A.

I imagined the water was clear, crystal blue, and I could see all the way down to the bottom without fear of being swallowed up. It was chlorinated, clean, purifying, and baptismal—in a Jewish sort of way.

I sat down on the float to get a bit of sun and to begin my meditation. A little while later Lara came outside.

"The pool looks great," she laughed at me, then switched to her older sister voice to add, "but you look a little thin."

"I need to look good in my bathing suit," I said, resorting to my black-humor voice that was coming out more and more as I descended deeper into the cancer ordeal.

"Very funny. You need to eat."

"I will when my appetite comes back." Then I changed the subject.

"Do you remember when all the kids learned how to swim in my pool? I bought those inflatable boats, paddles, buckets, and squirt guns, and we played Boat War, trying to drown each other. Those were the best days." They really were. Maybe it was the Pisces thing.

"Yes, they were, but getting back to the point. You can't keep up your strength if you don't eat."

"Okay, Mom," I told her, which is exactly what she was being, and I loved it.

"What's the rash all over your back?" Lara asked.

"It's probably a reaction to the meds. It itches like

hell." I wish she hadn't reminded me. Now I couldn't stop scratching, probably because she'd drawn attention to it, which was again like the elephant in the room that you can't stop thinking about.

"Really? Or it could be the dogs; they're scratching too? Come in the house," she suggested. "I'll put some ointment on it."

It was wonderful to have her there. My deep sense of isolation was less painful with her around, and her presence was enough to make me feel optimistic about getting through the ordeal. She visited so frequently that when she wasn't visiting, I just imagined that she was.

My daughter, Dina, was now studying at U.C. Berkeley and was in and out of our house. The last few years had been hardest on her. She was loving and kind, but stressed, as one would expect. Jake, now nineteen, was on a break from school and taking a lot of cooking classes, which he loved. I kept encouraging him to take classes at Le Cordon Bleu. He was thinking about becoming a chef and opening his own restaurant one day.

Personally, I dreaded cooking, because it was so time-consuming, an energy drainer. I thought of everything in my life in terms of the "ergs of energy" they required, and tried to conserve my ergs for what was most important to me in life. But Jake loved cooking up a storm for everyone, though I couldn't eat anything.

It was fun to watch him. He had always been so active,

and whenever he was in the kitchen there was a lot of banging of pots, pans, cabinets, dishes, and silverware. You name it, and he banged it around. In a strange way, all his noise brought me peace and reminded me that life was brimming all around me. I imagined he'd either become a drummer, like his mom, or a chef.

As Lara was applying Benadryl, both kids walked in the back door. That was the first time I would experience what I call "Action/Cut" syndrome. I would be in the midst of a situation that to me had some degree of drama or comedy to it as if I were a character in a play, TV series, or movie. In my director's mind, I would shout "Action!" when it started, and "Cut!" when I wanted it to end. I began thinking of everything in life as a scene. The next series of events felt like a bunch of rapid-fire "Action/Cuts," which I mentally cataloged as loving chaos scenes.

Moreover, *I began to realize that there is absolutely nothing funny about cancer, but funny things do happen to those with cancer.* I began paying closer attention to and relishing in the funny and curious things happening to me as I learned to cope with my own disease. "Find what's funny" became another mantra of mine, and I did.

"Action!" I yelled to myself, feeling like a movie director.

Jake entered the kitchen with a basketball in his hands.

"Think fast, everyone!" Jake yelled. He threw the ball, which boomeranged off the walls and landed right into my newly organized box of medications. Hundreds of pills went flying, ricocheting all around the room, as both dogs lunged after them.

"Jake!" we all yelled.

"Kids, get the dogs. We'll get the pills." Pandemonium ensued. It took a while to find all of the pills, which then needed to be counted and sorted back into their individual containers. Jake sheepishly came over to me.

"Sorry, Mom," he said. His long sigh told me he meant it.

"Nice shot, Kobe," Dina taunted him.

"How about next time you think first, instead of think fast," I implored, and then said it again to myself.

"Cut!" I shouted in my director's head.

As the day progressed I noticed the dogs were constantly famished and staring at the walls, as it suddenly occurred to me what was going on, I recounted the synthetic and very mild marijuana pills that the doctor had given me for nausea, and found a few were missing. The dogs were stoned, but the kids kept tricking them by moving their beds and feeding bowls around the house. I immediately called the vet to make sure they would be OK, but actually, I have to admit it was kind of funny.

Lara and Dina began reorganizing the meds.

"Action!" I yelled again in my head again.

"When you organize medications, you set them up in morning, afternoon, and evening piles," Lara said. "And then you know when to take them."

"No, they should be clearly marked and kept in alphabetical order. With a little chart and boxes so you can check them off."

"I was a nurse," Lara started to explain, trying to hold back from her form of a lecture.

"Who's going to be giving her these medications when you're gone? I need to know where they are," Dina replied. Her voice was getting frosty.

"I'm not going anywhere today, honey!"

Things were escalating, and I was beginning to get stressed again."

"Please stop!" I begged. With all their great intentions, I just wanted peace, and I was banging my head against the kitchen wall this time.

"Fine, do it your way." Dina gave in.

"Cut!"

🎗🎗🎗

The next morning as I walked downstairs in my bare feet, I was greeted by a yellow mess in the middle of the floor. No one else had noticed it, and I stepped right into it.

"Action!" Instinctively, I reverted to director mode.

"OK, you two!" I snapped. "Get over here now!"

Everyone came running downstairs, not realizing I was talking to the dogs.

"Shit. What did you do this time?" Dina said to Jake.

"Me? What did *you do?*" he replied.

"We're going to have a serious discussion." They all froze.

"You know I'm not well, and this is how you treat me, after everything I've done for the both of you?"

Everyone was confused.

I cried, "Both of you, just...shit all over me, in my own house? How do you think that makes me feel? Well...how?"

No one dared to speak. I looked down at the dogs in anger.

"Just get out now...I don't even want to look at you. I'll send you both to the glue factory. Get out!!"

The two little Bichon Frises, who knew they were to blame, quickly tore out through the doggy door. Lara gestured to the kids to clean the mess.

"It's okay, Mom, we'll take care of it," Dina said.

"Cut!"

"Hey, Nan, let's sit outside," Lara said, trying to be the peacemaker as she led me outside.

"Aaaaccction!"

"I'm so glad you're here," I told her. It was her umpteenth visit.

"Me too," she said. "They're under a lot of stress too, you know."

"They really are. I told the doctor that. The nervousness, whining and itching—I can't deal with all of it. The doctor said he could give me steroids or Prozac, but not both. I told him I would give them the steroids, and if they couldn't take the Prozac then I would take it."

"What the hell are you talking about?" she asked.

"The dogs. What are you talking about?"

"Not the dogs!" she said, laughing. "Your kids!"

"Oh…them," I said. Of course, I thought, and then smacked my head with my hand.

"Cut!"

���

As a theatre director, my instincts were always to view my life as an unfolding story, and it served me well during my illness. Everything became fodder for an evolving story, a drama or comedy. I wanted to write it or, better yet, direct this show. That's the role I'm used to, being in charge.

"I want to make sure that you're okay when I leave next week." Lara said. I couldn't bear for her to leave, but she had her own family. Stanley and the two boys whom I love and adore have always been wonderful to me. I had always been close to her boys, just like my brother's kids.

I laugh every time I think about our six kids when they were younger, making a choo-choo train out of my mom's mobility scooter and all the wheelchairs they could find in the retirement home where she lived. They would ride it up and down the hallways, smiling and waving at all the elderly residents, who would blankly smile and wave back in kind. The kids were becoming indoctrinated to the family philosophy of laughing in the face of illness whenever possible. We encouraged it.

Everyone was trying so hard now, but with all I'd been through, I felt like one of those Whack-A-Mole toys after you clobber them. I was wobbly, and my head thumping wasn't making it better. I was standing at the cliff's edge of sanity. I knew I was irritable and snapping, which I felt bad about, but I couldn't control it.

My pool meditations were helping, but they weren't enough. I was clearly on edge. I needed something more. I promised Lara that I would discuss it with the doctor, whom I was scheduled to see after she left.

7

SativaIndicaHybrid

The curious prescription I held in my hand the next week was for the medicinal use of real marijuana, no fake pills. I was embarrassed. I hadn't actually smoked marijuana since college in the '70s.

"What do I do with this?" I asked the doctor.

"There is a place in the Haight-Ashbury." I had to laugh. "The Haight," as everybody in the Bay Area calls it, had been the epicenter of the cultural revolution of the '60s, and was still a magnet for hippies and dropouts from all over the world.

I knew I wasn't going there alone; it was not a safe place, as I recalled. I would have to find someone to go with me, but I was way too embarrassed to ask my friends, and at the same time I was desperate for relief. The following day, Jake found the prescription that I accidentally left sitting on the kitchen counter.

"Wow! Is this for real? Score, Mom!" Jake asked.

"Where are you going to get it?"

Shit. I was busted and felt embarrassed, but there was no escaping it.

"Dunno, the Haight?"

His eyes lit up, and a smirk ran across his face. I knew it was a mistake to talk about this with him; he loved that he had busted me. What a role reversal!

"Look, can we be adult about this?" I asked.

"Hell, yeah. I'll take you." I hadn't even asked.

"You do understand that you aren't allowed to buy anything?"

"Yeah, yeah. Sure, whatever. Let's go."

The next thing I knew, we were in my silver roadster pulling up to a legal but seedy pot club right on Haight Street, near Golden Gate Park. There were a lot of unsavory people loitering on the street in front of the shop. Being very self-conscious, I put on my sunglasses and a hat, looking more like Jackie Onassis than Janis Joplin, who had actually lived nearby.

"We're going in," my son said in a gangsta voice, and again laughed at his ridiculous mother, now wearing a disguise. He put on his shades too.

We entered the psychedelic-looking and very surreal shop. It was a time warp transporting me back to the '60s. Three or four very stoned young guys in filthy jeans and reeking of pot were slowly browsing the long display case. It was crammed with multicolored glass pipes, rolling papers, hookahs, and God knows what else. A skinny guy with a beard stood behind the counter.

He asked Jake, "Dude, do you have a doctor's letter?"

Jake laughed, and said, "It's not for me," pointing to me. "It's for my mom." The guy behind the counter tried to stifle his laughter, but couldn't, and started choking.

Jake ran his hand along the glass, salivating over the display case, as I handed the guy my letter, which he didn't even read before pointing me to the back of the store. When we both turned to go there, the kid barked to Jake, "Dude, not you! Just your mom." He started choking again.

Jake was disappointed, but happily drooling over the glass case with its various colorful marijuana accessories.

"Don't sell him anything while I'm gone!" I blurted out, trying to scare the guy. From the way he looked at us, I'm pretty sure we were the only mother/son duo he'd ever dealt with. He was beyond amused.

At the back of the store was a locked metal door, the kind they have to buzz to get you access to the sanctuary. A heavyset, bearded, and heavily tattooed bouncer-looking guy sat at that door. Though I knew this was legal, it sure didn't feel like it. And on the top of that, I was feeling guilty about allowing my son to escort me here, and worried about what he was up to in the other room. It was odd after trying to protect him from drugs when he was younger that we were now in a dope den together—well, what felt like one to me.

The bouncer let me through the heavy metal door. Inside was a glass window with a little hole, the kind of peephole you might see in an old movie theatre. This place was creeping me out.

"Wait here," he said, and left, slamming the heavy door behind him.

I waited back there for several minutes until, to my complete and utter astonishment, a woman in a burka appeared. Of all things, I never expected that.

"Carpeeze," she said, in a foreign accent.

I had no idea what she just said. I tried to guess her ethnicity by her accent. I would say she sounded East Indian, but I thought they didn't do marijuana.

"Excuse me??"

"Medicamarijuanacarpeeze." Everything she said sounded exactly the same, and like one long muffled word through the glass window and her burka.

"Huh?" I said as she pointed at the letter in my hand.

"Drivalicenz?"

Ah! I handed her my license.

"Sativaindicahybrid?"

"What??" I seriously expected the *Candid Camera* crew to bust thru the door.

"Sativaindicahybrid?" I don't know why she thought repeating and saying it louder would help.

"Okay, whatever." I was clueless.

"Which one?" She was getting irritated with me.

"You choose." I smiled politely.

"Hybrid."

"Perfect." I smiled again, still clueless.

"How much?" she demanded to know.

I gestured several inches with my thumb and middle finger.

"Tumuch. Illigal."

"Okay…got that …whatever you think."

She pulled out two plastic bags and put her hand through the small window.

"Vezamstrcrdormericnspress."

"What?"

"Veza…mstrcrd…mericnspress."

"Ah, finally, the universal language," I thought, and whipped out my credit card.

"How much is that?"

"Wunhndrdfefty."

"Yikes." That would have cost me $20 in 1972, I thought.

She snatched the card out of my hand, swiped it, and handed it back before I could blink. She also handed me the two small baggies.

"Go now!" she shouted. I left the room at her command. She scared the hell out of me.

"Let's go," I said to Jake.

"Just a minute." Jake was stuffing something in his pocket.

"Hey, didn't I tell you not to sell him anything?" I yelled to the guy behind the counter.

"It's nothing, really, just papers," he said.

"NOW!" I insisted.

"Yeah, yeah, I'm coming," Jake said as I grabbed his arm.

We hopped in the car.

"Let me see what you got." Jake grabbed the bag from my hand before I could say "no!"

"Holy shit, mom! You did it. You scored, Mom!" He was giddy.

"Wipe that smile off your face." Which he did, mostly.

"Can I have....?"

"No!"

"But...."

"Drive!"

He revved up the roadster, and we headed home. Whatever else my kids thought of me, I wasn't stupid. I'd had already installed a safe in my home.

Wouldn't you know it? My kids suddenly became my new best friends. Now in college, I couldn't stop them from smoking pot with their friends, but I would make certain that they kept their grubby little hands off my stash. There was no way I could hide it from them, so I tried to be open, but not indulgent. I would find them nonchalantly looking through the pantry, closets, and bathrooms.

"Whatcha looking for, Jake?" I asked him when I found him rummaging through cereal boxes at 9 p.m.

"Oh, nothing, Mom," he slurred. "Just hungry."

"You won't find it," I said as I walked through the kitchen without stopping.

"Come on, Mom," I heard as I headed up the stairs. My daughter followed me.

"Forget it, Sweetie," I told her as she was ransacking my bathroom.

"I'm just looking for some mascara, Mom."

"You know I don't wear it. It makes me cry. Just put everything back the way you found it, please."

"You know you can trust me, Mom. Where is it?" She said it ever so sweetly, trying to get on my good side.

"Bye," I told her as I steered her out of the bathroom and locked the door. The nausea was back, and my head was spinning from not having eaten.

I turned on the shower water and vent to get rid of the smell, and I sat on the floor of the bathroom, lighting up a joint.

"I know what you are doing!" Dina yelled at me, and she ran to get Jake. They both returned a moment later. I heard them whispering on the other side of the door.

"We want to help you, Mom." The kindness in his voice and this lovely gesture tugged at my heartstrings.

I was reminded of when I was first diagnosed and they were sixteen and seventeen and both ensconced in school. We were having a discussion, and in earnest they said they wanted to help me by taking me to my doctors "on evenings and weekends." It was truly endearing, but my burst of laughter left them completely bewildered. I was nonetheless deeply touched.

Now, I heard more whispering.

"I can't help you the way other people can," Jake said in a tone of voice I hadn't heard before. " Please, Mom, let me help you the way I know how."

"Let him, Mom!" she pleaded

"The way I know how?" What the hell did that mean? But, I was proud of them for caring.

"What exactly do you mean?" I asked.

"I want to cook for you," Jake blurted.

"How sweet." Of course, the best way he knew. I wanted to cry with pride.

I had encouraged his joy of cooking, just as I had always urged both of my children to find what they loved to do and figure out how to make a living at it, as I had done. "That way you are never really working," I explained many times. "So many people hate what they do, and that's sad."

"So you'll let me cook for you?" he asked. "Anything you want."

"But I'm not hungry, and I have no appetite," I said.

"I can fix that," he said.

"You can fix that?" I asked. I cracked the door as I tried to blow away the smoke.

"Brownies—I want to make you some brownies," he said in earnest.

"I can't eat brownies right now." As I said that, I realized where this conversation was headed. But what kind of sucker did my kids think I was?

"Marijuana brownies." He tried to hide his devilish smile. I slammed the door closed.

"NO! I am not giving you my stash."

"Just this once, Mom," she begged.

"NO!!" I shouted again.

Jake has always been the most persistent person I've ever known. He'd make a great salesman, I thought.

"Come on, Mom…."

"Nooo!"

"Pleeeaaasssse!"

"Mom, let him," Dina said. She was sensible, and maybe she knew something I didn't. I realized this would go on all night; I didn't want to sleep in the bathroom, and was just too tired to argue with him.

"Well…okay…just this one time." I slowly opened the door.

"You won't be sorry," he promised. I already was. They ecstatically ran downstairs together.

"Yeah…right," I thought. I went to my safe, opened

it, and pulled out one of the little baggies of pot.

They were both so excited. I could hear them downstairs. They sounded like happy little chirping birds. Then, Jake began whistling and singing, and pulling out pots and pans. He commenced with his usually banging and slamming of everything in the kitchen. It made me laugh that he was so predictable. I came downstairs with one of the little plastic baggies. He was melting butter on the stove. I handed him the weed, and he dumped the entire bag in the butter.

"Oh my God—what are you doing?"

"You have to cook the pot first."

"No, you don't! We just put in the brownie mix." Ooops! I had just revealed more than I wanted to about my past.

He smiled, and stirred the disgusting-looking green concoction, then started to sing again. I went upstairs to lie down. Twenty minutes later when I went back downstairs to check on him, he was straining the marijuana and letting the butter drip into the brownie mix. I watched in horror as he threw the drenched marijuana in the trash.

"Seriously...you just threw that away?" I was pissed.

"Trust me!" I never, ever trusted him. It always led to trouble.

"He knows what he's doing," Dina said proudly.

"This is crazy." I went back upstairs. A while later, the

aroma of baking brownies wafted into the bedroom and woke me up. It smelled delicious, and I was drawn back down to the kitchen. Dina had gone over to her friend's for the night.

I love to see a man cook. I'd only known a few men who could do more than barbecue a hot dog. He moved around the kitchen gracefully and confidently, singing the entire time. His body had been in constant motion since he was born.

"They have to cool for 20 minutes," he said.

I have to admit I was getting a kick out of seeing him do this. Actually, it was downright adorable. Then he even started cleaning up the mess, which shocked me, since cleaning was not his forte. My baby's growing up, I thought.

After the brownies had cooled, he cut them into very precise squares. He took out the plastic wrap and began carefully wrapping each of the dozen or so brownies very neatly, tucking, tucking, and folding the corners. He reminded me of Michael Keaton's hilarious character fastidiously cooking in the movie *Multiplicity*. I was impressed, and gave him a big hug and kiss.

"Thanks, Jake, I really appreciate it. I love you. I'm going to bed."

Fifteen minutes or so later, he came up to my room.

"I'm leaving now," he said. He too was spending the night at a friend's apartment. He leaned over and kissed me goodbye. I always missed him when he was away at school.

"Thanks again," I told him.

"I put the brownies in the freezer, Mom. Call me tomorrow and let me know what you think."

"I will. I love you." He let himself out, and I went to sleep.

The next morning, I awoke feeling nauseous as usual. I went down to the kitchen to make my Italian roast. I was hungry, but had no desire to eat. Then I remembered the brownies. I tried to remember where he said he'd put them? The freezer?

I opened the freezer door, and a bunch of food fell out onto the floor. Jake had certainly been here, I laughed to myself. I saw a brownie, and grabbed it.

Over the years, I had kept all our sweets, cookies, and cakes, in the freezer to slow down my family's consumption. All that really happened was that we all learned to enjoy frozen desserts, and everything disappeared just as quickly as if it had been in the pantry. To this day, I love frozen cookies.

Throughout the day, I nibbled on my brownie, which miraculously seemed to help the nausea and my appetite. Later in the day, I went to the freezer to grab another one. I looked everywhere, took everything out of the freezer, but didn't find them. I called Jake.

"Hi, Mom! Didya like the brownies?" He asked enthusiastically.

"Actually, I think they helped!" He was totally shocked.

"They taste a little weird, but I have to say they helped."

"Really? I told you that you could trust me." He was very proud of himself.

"I misjudged you. I'm sorry for that."

"Thanks, Mom," he said. "Gotta go!"

"Wait, I can't find the others. Where did you put them?"

He hesitated.

"I got to go, Mom."

"But where did you say you put them?"

"Well, I really didn't think you'd like them, so I took them with me. Got to go. Love you."

He quickly hung up.

After banging my head against the refrigerator a few times, I thought, Duh???? Of course he did. And then I did the only thing I could. I laughed...for the rest of the day. In fact, it was the best laugh I'd had in a long time.

I loved being their mom, and it reminded me that that was what I was living for.

8

Shrink Writing

After my cancer diagnosis and separation, I felt that I needed therapy to deal with all the stress. I bounced around trying to find someone I was comfortable with, but to be honest, talk therapy didn't seem to help. The standard response from therapists was always the same: "How does that make you feel?" It didn't take a rocket scientist to understand that I felt terrible about all that I had lost in my life: health, career, marriage, and home. Essentially, I had lost everything except my kids, but they were truly what mattered most in my life.

I was beginning to feel that I could get as much out of asking myself the same question and simply recording my answer. I had gone on hoping against hope that the therapist would simply tell me what to do. But, of course, therapy doesn't work that way, at least the kind I needed at the time. I needed a thorough reboot, like a computer gone haywire.

In the several visits of talk therapy that I had with Dr. Marcus, we had only talked about my health, divorce, and kids. I had not yet mentioned my extensive background in theatre arts.

"Can I write something to read to you next time instead of talking?"

"Write? I'm not sure I know what you mean?" he replied, genuinely surprised.

I explained to him that I wanted to use my lifelong experience in theatre and writing to help with my struggle to survive or die, whatever was meant to be. I was interested in writing as a form of self-help therapy. Also, my extensive background studying Psychodrama in graduate school, a form of theatre therapy, made me think that this could be useful.

He agreed, but wanted to know more about my background so that he could help as much as possible. I began the tale.

ⵝ ⵝ ⵝ

When I was twelve and we moved from Chicago to L.A. my parents followed my aunt and uncle, who had moved there years earlier for the health of their polio-stricken son. They chose Beverly Hills because of the exemplary school system, like many other families.

Their decision to do so changed my life. We lived in a rented duplex south of Olympic Boulevard, otherwise known as the "slums of Beverly Hills."

I started high school the following year in 1966 when I was thirteen, because I had skipped a year. I was also very petite and felt out of my element in Beverly Hills as a kid from the south side of Chicago.

John Ingle, known later in life as Edward Quartermaine of *General Hospital* TV soap opera fame, was the drama teacher at Beverly Hills High at the time. He had a fabulous reputation, and had already taught Richard Dreyfuss, Rob Reiner, Albert Brooks, and many others who went on to become very successful.

John ignited my passion for theatre on my very first day of ninth grade, as he did with countless other students. I still remember the room number—176. I decided right then and there to become a drama teacher, but not just anywhere. I vowed to teach right there, at Beverly, and that vision became a motivating force in my life. A mentor is a powerful individual in a student's life, and I was blessed to have had the very finest in John.

After graduating from Beverly Hills High, I studied theatre at UCLA, and after graduating from there, spent time at the Royal Academy of Dramatic Art (RADA) in London. It was considered the most prestigious theatre school in the world at the time, and probably still is, a place where some of the greatest actors of many generations cut their teeth.

I also went nearly every evening and purchased the cheapest seats for live shows in London. I remember a spectacular new show called *A Chorus Line*, which took the theatre world by storm.

Upon my return home, I was in overdrive, as I completed an M.A. and several teaching credentials, and studied Psychodrama with one of its pioneers, Dr. Lewis Yablonsky.

I was also hired to teach Children's and Adult Theatre by both Beverly Hills Cultural Affairs and the City of Los Angeles. Both of the wonderful women who hired me became great friends.

It was a very busy time and I was burning the candle at both ends, but I loved every minute. I was thrilled to have found my passion and a way to support myself doing what I felt I was born to do.

Then when the time came for my student teaching assignment, John went to bat for me to recruit me as his student teacher at Beverly.

The following semester, and ten years from that fateful day that I first walked into John's class as a freshman, he handed me the keys to the very same room 176—to begin my teaching career in theatre at Beverly. It felt like winning the lottery to me.

Over the years, the Performing Arts department had grown tremendously in size and popularity and was one of the school district's most coveted programs, and unlike any other program in the country.

A number of our students came from celebrity families, and looking into the audiences at our shows there were countless notable actors, directors, producers, agents, and casting directors. Many other students came from regular homes or were bussed into the district. For most of the students, our department became a surrogate family and another home, a place where they could find their passions and thrive. I would usually be at school late into the evening and find kids still rehearsing, or just sitting in the theatre eating "McD's" as they called it. At 9 p.m. I lovingly kicked them out, sent them home, and locked the doors, only to return at 7 a.m. to let them back in and begin another magical day.

Among our students were Nicholas Cage, David Schwimmer, and director Jon Turteltaub of *While You Were Sleeping*. I was pleased to induct Jon in Beverly's Hall of Fame two years ago. We also taught the future creators of *Weeds, Orange Is the New Black, Will and Grace* and many others. The real people that *Will and Grace* was based on were my students in my ninth grade Shakespeare program. Max Mutchnick, the show's openly gay producer, acknowledged basing the show on his relationship with his then girlfriend, Janet. I adored them both. The list goes on and on.

The students were immensely talented and hard-working, and we all strived for excellence in every endeavor: musicals, dramas, Shakespeare, and the rest. It was a magical time and place, and countless students went on to create their own far-reaching accomplishments.

Although it was glamorous and exciting, I didn't think of it that way at the time. I was too busy working: teaching acting, directing, tech theatre, dramatic writing, and directing performances. I wrote and directed numerous original pieces and adapted others, including 10-minute versions of Shakespeare's most popular plays for students to perform. Shakespeare has always been another passion of mine.

The back of a theatre became my very favorite spot in life because from there I could have an overarching view, seeing my work performed live and its real-time impact both on the actors and audience.

I was also elected to become the president of the Drama Teachers' Association of Southern California, the youngest ever, and organized competitive events for all the participating schools and their students, which was immensely rewarding.

I remember one day standing at the back of the auditorium where my students were performing their winning scenes on stage in front of over a thousand competitors from all over Southern California.

As I watched, I suddenly and uncontrollably began to cry. I was overjoyed at the thought of all the thousand-plus students, from all walks of life, spending that beautiful spring day inside, performing Shakespeare. They might otherwise be out on the streets doing drugs, drinking, or getting into trouble. However, safely ensconced in our program here they were all screaming, cheering, and applauding each other over Shakespeare. It was almost like a dream, and one of the most glorious memories I have of my teaching career.

When John passed away several years ago in his eighties and more than twenty-five years after he retired from Beverly, a Facebook page was started by one of our former students and my dear friend, Liz. Roughly six hundred of his/our former students mourned online for weeks, and most returned to Beverly for a memorial to honor him weeks later. He was a man whom I truly loved, admired, and who changed my life in the most wonderful way. I am ever grateful to him for that.

It also gave me an opportunity to reconnect with hundreds of my former students, many of whom remain my close and loving friends. As a young teacher, I always felt like I was more an older sister to my students than their teacher. It's hard for me to imagine a more rewarding profession, and those years at Beverly remain one of the highlights of my life.

During my tenure at Beverly, I was married and had two beautiful children, eighteen months apart. I was immensely happy, and felt that "I had it all." Unfortunately, I was later diagnosed with Lupus, a seriously debilitating disease, which forced me to stop working. Not being able to teach there anymore nearly broke my heart. However, the silver lining was that it gave me more precious time to spend with my kids.

ℛ ℛ ℛ

In 1991, as my kids began school, we moved to beautiful Marin County. The enervating disease continued to prevent me from teaching, and by then I simply hated not working at all. As soon as I was able to regain some strength, I resumed teaching part-time at the American Conservatory Theater, San Francisco's premier theatre school, which had a wonderful youth conservatory. I thoroughly enjoyed being part of it.

I also directed plays at my children's schools. They included almost the entire student body of up to three hundred children. I was able to do it with the help of countless parents who couldn't have been more generous with their time, commitment, and money. After a number of fantastic shows, I could not sustain my energy to continue to do that, which repeated yet again a difficult disappointment in my life. After taking care of my family, I had precious few little "ergs" of energy left for creativity.

But now there was an interesting twist: the parents who had helped me with the kids' shows were now insisting in starring in their own shows. They were eager to convert my three-car garage into a theatre studio, so I didn't even have to leave the house, which made it perfect for me—and I was elated. We erected a stage, hung theatre lights and sound equipment. We hung a bulletin board on the door of the old refrigerator, and my troupers signed up to rehearse in small groups or individually with me. The refrigerator was well stocked with water and, most importantly, wine. Our hilarious happy hour rehearsals often ran late into the evening. Our troupe became the talk of the town, and I was thrilled to launch this new adult community theatre.

Best of all, our children, all of whom had been in my productions, became our tech crew in recompense for the hard work their parents had done for their shows. The kids ran lights and sound, helped build the sets and props. The parents and their children had a blast working together. It was amazing to behold, and I was very proud of the extraordinary camaraderie that I was able to foster within our community.

We informally became known as "The Garage People." Neighbors used to listen outside the garage to the uproarious laughter and antics emanating from within. Rather than call the police for disturbing the peace, they let me know how much joy our theatre performances were bringing to the town. Tickets for our shows sold out way in advance, and we donated all our proceeds every year to charities. It was a win-win for everyone, especially me.

Over that fabulous period, I wrote or adapted countless one-act plays and lumped ten or so of them together for our productions. Most were outrageous comedies, like the one we called Superheroes, about a group of blundering female superheroes in capes and masks who were drawn into ineptitude because they were all afraid of their own shadows. I always sprinkled into our productions one or two poignant, serious pieces that created a roller coaster experience of laughter and tears. I have always loved juxtaposing comedies with dramatic pieces.

Klezmer is Eastern European music, which I had never really listened to before. A theatre trouper of mine, a doctor by day and musician at night, needed a drummer for his band. Why he asked me was beyond me, since I had never played the drums. Nevertheless, I erected a big yellow drum set in my living room next to my piano where the band rehearsed, and I learned to play them. It was a hoot!

As a child, I loved watching my mother sculpt and paint. It had a profound effect on me. I always wanted a home filled with passion and the arts for my children, which I can truly say that I did provide. For years, our home became an ongoing symphony of theatre, music, dance, and song.

My creativity had also served as an outlet for stress in my life, as well as an aspect of my determination to cobble together the most life-affirming existence possible. Creativity has always been for me what air and water are to others, necessary for the maintenance and survival of life. More than anything, it was vegetarian chicken soup for my battered soul, without which I felt there could be very little "quality of life" in mine.

⚯⚯⚯

After explaining all of this to Dr. Marcus, he understood that I wanted to do exactly what Dr. Frankl had done, and for the same reasons. If the writing had gotten him through the living hell of the concentration camps, perhaps it would help me harrow my own hell.

Dr. Marcus seemed intrigued, and for the following appointment I brought in a scene that I had written, and began to read it to him. He listened intently.

"It was really hot outside," I began tentatively, "even though it was late afternoon. I decided to cool off in the pool." I took a deep breath and went on. "I went down the steps into the water and something was, um, off."

"Off?" replied the therapist in my scene.

"Yeah, the water. It was yellow. At first, I thought it was urine…in the pool. I stepped back quickly and fell into the pool. I started to gag and choke, and then all of a sudden I realized the water was sweet and familiar."

"What was it?"

"I tasted it. It was lemonade. The entire pool was filled with lemonade."

"Lemonade? Really? Well, what do you make of that?"

Of course, he would say that. I laughed to myself.

"Well…I thought about it for a long time. And then—bang—it hit me. You know how people always say, 'When life gives you lemons, make lemonade'?"

"Sure, it's a common expression."

"The entire pool was filled with all the goddamned lemonade I've been making for years. Was my psyche trying to tell me I've been up to my neck in lemonade?"

"So what do you think of that?" he challenged me.

"You tell me!" I demanded.

"Therapy doesn't work like that. You know that."

Dyslexia had become another fun new side effect of medications too. Glancing at the title of a book on his shelf, I blurted out "The rapist"?

"What?"

"Oh!" I said, looking at the word a second time. "Oh, sorry. It says 'Therapist'; have you ever noticed that?"

"Ouch!" he yelped.

"I just realized it." I felt badly that I had implied anything horrible.

"Well, Freud might disagree." He laughed. "But we won't tell him."

"I'm just so tired…exhausted really…of having to make the best of a bad situation. Can't anything just be good without my having to break my back?"

"What do you mean, Nancy?"

"I look around at other people I know and their lives just seem to, I don't know, just happen effortlessly. My life takes so much effort. I guess I'm a little jealous of other people around me."

"Well, things aren't always as they..."

"Stop. I know what you're going to say. Everyone has his or her own problems that are true. I'm not disagreeing with you. But it is also a matter of the size of your problems, and how much they consume of your life. And, well, mine consume a lot."

"So where does that leave you?"

"Wanting to switch lives with someone else!"

He chuckled at me and said, "Anyone in particular?"

"Let's just say a lot of people," I sighed.

"And since you know you can't do that, what are you going to do?"

"I really don't know. I suppose I'll just have to keep squeezing more lemons."

By the time I finished reading my scene, the puzzled look on Dr. Marcus's face changed to one of understanding.

"I think writing is very good for you. Would you be willing to write and share something else next week?" I smiled.

♊ ♊ ♊

At dawn the next morning, I eagerly sat down in my lounge chair with my Italian roast and began writing a series of short scenes about cancer, chemo, kids, divorce, abandonment, the pool, the family dogs, my students, the Vespa, medicinal marijuana, camping on the beach. I wrote about everything that meant anything to me, which all become fodder for the scenes. I found that writing about my life was actually helping me live it.

Often the lines between my reality, my dreams, and my hopes became fuzzy. Sometimes my writing would start as nonfiction and morph into a piece of fiction. I didn't think it mattered, because it was all born from my life anyway, as an expression of what had happened or not, but that I wanted to happen or change in some way. I gladly began writing for my therapist, and started referring to it all as my "shrink writing."

The other advantage to writing I called THE ZAP. If I didn't like the way something was unfolding in my life, I could ZAP it—just rewrite it and reframe my brain to the way I wanted it to be. If, for example, the kids weren't acting the way I wanted them to then—ZAP! And with the flash of my pen, I had new kids. I could do that with anyone or anything, and I did. It gave me back a sense of power that I had lost over my life. It was theatrical, dramatic, and it was fun.

And so, I kept an ongoing theatre in my head, ever on the lookout for finding what was funny or touching around me.

ЯЯЯ

Not long afterward, in 2006, I enrolled in a writing class,

which I really found interesting and a great challenge. I was so motivated when the class ended, I quickly enrolled in a university's certificated feature-film-writing program of ten classes, of which I took a number online. Other classes I took in person when I was in L.A. for treatments. I wrote "what I knew," which is generally what writers are advised to do.

I began writing a screenplay about my own authentic life, in which I portrayed myself as I was, a forty-something wife, mother of two teens, and teacher, who is suddenly diagnosed with Stage 4 cancer. She must overcome the shock of the death sentence, her children's conflicted reactions, and her husband's surprise walk-out. But, I would center the story around a therapeutic swimming pool, as I set out to live the last of my life on my own terms.

I called my new screenplay "Quality of Life." It was a natural title, since nearly all of the cancer treatment conversations I'd had with doctors ended with those three encouraging words. I thought it was the perfect description for a poignant and fresh story about love, laughter—and cancer, and that I would be the first to write a screenplay about those three seemingly unrelated words.

The disease wasn't even a topic commonly seen in TV or films. The 1983 movie *Terms of Endearment* was the only one I could think of, and that was more of a story about a mother's relationship with her dying daughter. Cancer was rather arbitrary in that story. It just happened to be the disease the daughter was suffering from.

There were two euphemisms I knew well from my father, who had died of lung cancer in his sixties, and others of his generation. One was the "C Word" and the other was "Big C." Although it may seem melodramatic by today's standards, "cancer" was a word that people dared not utter aloud back then, and when it was, it was only whispered.

Over the next three and a half years, I took all the classes, but only one per quarter. Each class was a tremendous amount of work, but I loved it. I was shocked to find that most of my instructors found my writing about cancer to be humorous in a dark way. They encouraged my writing about my life in the style I called "dramedy," part drama and part comedy. I had never heard anyone use that term before, which has since become a mainstream term. But, it was always my natural style of writing during difficult times.

In the fall of 2008, I took another online class with the writing program. That instructor was a prominent writer and also very spiritual, so our relationship seemed a perfect fit. Her name was Bonnie and she agreed, as the other teachers had, to work with me one-on-one through emails rather than posting assignments on a new university Internet blackboard system. She taught the class with a partner, but I worked mostly with Bonnie.

At this point, I was writing mostly for myself to heal and to gain some meaning, as Dr. Frankl had encouraged in his inspiring book. I wasn't ready to share it with others, as it was all deeply personal. I wanted to keep it very private, sharing it only with my instructors, at least until I had something that I was ready to make more public.

I also hoped that by the time I was finished with all the classes, I could sell my screenplay, and obviously didn't want anyone to steal it. I don't even know why that occurred to me. That was about as likely to happen as winning the lottery.

Working with Bonnie was fascinating. She had many insights into my writings. Every morning I would settle into my lounge chair with my Italian roast on the table next to me and spend hours writing. Every afternoon I would send her the best of what I had written that day. She would promptly respond with comments, some questions, and some suggestions.

More than that, she had the amazing gift of being able to reach inside my brain and heart, yank it out of me, and wrap it in a hug. She was able to pull writing out of me similar to the way I was able to yank performances out of my drama students.

By the time I finished the class, her teaching had not only changed my writing but had also changed my life. I found a strong connection between my writing, my ability to cope and, to some degree, to heal. I made it my goal, even when I felt terrible, to try to write at least a few pages every day. The writing kept me going.

Towards the end of the quarter, I had completed most of what would become my screenplay. I wasn't content with it by any stretch and certainly hadn't completed it. I was aware that it needed a lot of work, which meant rewriting and more rewriting. Moreover, the entire thing had been written while on chemo, radiation, and under the very strong effects of medical marijuana. To me, it was a personal, though barely yet woven together, episodic, hallucinogenic, emotional identity piece about a bizarre life that I was actually living.

As weird a story as it was, it was my unique story. More importantly, it was my version of what Dr. Frankl's book had been for him, his motivation for surviving.

No one could have grasped the magnitude to which my crazy, therapeutic, sad, funny, and outrageous writing had become my survival guide. And, of course, as all productions have been to me, it was my baby, to which I simply needed to give birth.

But, I didn't have an ending. I had resisted finishing the script because I wanted it to be truthful. That meant I was waiting to see what would happen to me. If at any point I felt that I was truly dying, then that's what I would write into my screenplay, and so my character too would die.

On the other hand, if I somehow continued to live beyond all expectation and statistics, then so too would my character, which would also give me an amazing opportunity to bring real hope to all those living with cancer. It was becoming increasingly clear to me that helping other cancer survivors was also a primary goal.

I was determined to finish it when I could, and dreamed of turning my story into something great like I had always been able to do in the theatre. I had no doubt whatsoever that my story was timely, fresh and important.

I sent most of what I had written to Bonnie throughout the quarter. Then I began sending the last of what I had written before Thanksgiving 2008, along with a lovely note telling her how much I enjoyed the class and wishing her a joyous Thanksgiving. Finally, I sent the final draft of the entire script—everything I had at that point—on December 2, 2008. I told her I wasn't finished with it yet, but would get back to it when I was feeling better. We vowed to keep in touch.

For now, it was time to focus on radiation treatments. In 2009, I was also contending with the very distressing housing bubble. This put me in another quandary, as I debated about whether to stay in Marin or return to L.A., the place I always considered home and still had family, friends, and of course where the entertainment industry was centered, which many of my friends were involved in.

In 2009, my children were in their early twenties and very busy with grad school and their own lives. I was thinking that L.A. would be a much easier place for me to live. By now the cancer in my spine began making the simple act of walking difficult for me. Living in a neighborhood that contained everything I needed within several blocks was enticing and becoming more necessary.

⚢ ⚢ ⚢

The next time I saw Dr. Marcus, he was excitedly awaiting my newest story. I shared one that I had written about my friend, Dr. Bill Atchley, whose Swiss wife, Annelies, was also a dear friend, teacher, and artist. She ran an "in and out" art studio in her basement, like my theatre troupe, and was one of my garage troupe members. We were kindred spirits.

When I realized that Dr. Bill, who was in his eighties, and I were on same monthly chemo drip, I offered to drive him to a chemo center closer to our homes. It was important to me that I followed Frankl's rule about being of service to others, despite my own ailments.

Annelies was enormously grateful, but it was also helpful for me to have a chemo buddy. Though I hadn't yet figured out how to do it, I wanted to make our chemo experiences fun. I had begun to feel increasingly isolated and Bill's company would be great for me as well.

I picked up Bill in a top-down convertible, which he loved.

"Oh goody...top down," he said, "Watch this."

This handsome, charming, white-haired octogenarian hopped into the car like James Bond. Dr. Bill was a retired chief of staff and internist at a major university hospital. Bill told me about his father, who had been a distinguished doctor and an intellectual. He hung out with Lillian Hellman, who wrote "The Little Foxes" and many other classics, and was one of my favorite playwrights. Her lover was Dashiell Hammett, the legendary author of *The Maltese Falcon*. They were both part of a famous crowd of notorious rapscallion artists of which Dr. Bill's father had been part.

"The apple doesn't fall far from the tree," I told him. He seemed flattered. Dr. Bill was a man who was ahead of his time. He had won honors for his decades of commitment to the environment, wetlands, hybrid cars, and ozone and greenhouse gas issues. He often joked, "Al Gore stole my PowerPoint presentation."

As I drove, he would school me on global warming, politics, and the like. His worldliness was beyond impressive and quite fascinating. I think he was one of the smartest people I've ever known.

When we got to the infusion center, the nurses fought over my gracious and handsome friend, knowing that he was a prestigious doctor. They lost out to one of the elderly nurses; I referred to her as Nurse Ratched, the cold battle-axe nurse from Ken Kesey's classic book and eventual movie about an insane asylum, *One Flew Over the Cuckoo's Nest,* played by the brilliant actress Louise Fletcher. She ignored me, preferring to swoon over Dr. Bill, who was embarrassed.

"Could you please start our drips at the same time?" I asked.

"Why?" Nurse Ratched asked coldly. She was not amused.

"So we can race our drips for kicks!" She looked at me with disbelief. However, Bill's eyes lit up, and everyone in the room laughed, so she relented with a loud grunt.

"One, two, three…go!" I shouted.

Ratched and the other nurse opened the valves, and off we went to the races. I noticed her slightly adjusting Dr. Bill's chemo to drip a little faster. I didn't care. The truth is, anyone who can do that kind of work is quite simply an absolute saint as far as I'm concerned, including Nurse Ratched.

While the nurses and patients placed bets, Dr. Bill and I decided upon our wager. I suggested that the loser buys Irish Coffee for the winner at San Francisco's landmark Buena Vista Café. He loved the idea, and agreed so eagerly that our treatment became exactly the kind of playful competition that I hoped would make our excursions fun. Together, we raced our drips for the next two hours down to the very last drop. Bill won, and giggled like a kid.

One of the other patients, a heavyset, upbeat African-American woman with a jolly laugh, had been enthusiastically betting on me to win. Her name was Shirley. She offered me a consolation prize when I lost.

"Take this scarf. Someone gave it to me. You give it to some else when you're ready." From that day on we thought of ourselves as the "Sisterhood of the Traveling Scarves," our version of Ann Brashares's popular book and movie, *The Sisterhood of the Traveling Pants*.

"The Force be with you," she joked as she handed it to me.

Ratched remained to stay with Dr. Bill. She unhooked him and continued to flirt with him for what seemed like another hour. All the while the needle was still sticking out of my arm and beginning to hurt a little. She paid no attention. Dr. Bill asked her several times to unhook me, but she was too busy chatting him up to hear. I patiently sat there like a pincushion until it was time for her to take her lunch, and one of the other nurses came over to unstick me.

The Buena Vista is a beloved century-old bar and one of my favorite watering holes in San Francisco. It has a charming throwback ambiance; friendly, shared tables; and a worldly crowd of locals and tourists. The BV, as locals call it, sits on the corner of Beach and Hyde, across from Aquatic Park, where the cable cars turn around overlooking the Bay. According to local legend, Irish Coffee was invented at the Buena Vista, although other bars around the world claim the same honor. Regardless, as far as I'm concerned, they are the absolutely best, and the views are world class.

Nevertheless, Bill and I were very aware of the ever-ticking time bomb or "The Return of the Irish Coffee," as we called it. But we drank anyway. We both had too much to be thankful for, so we toasted to another month of life. After sitting and unwinding for exactly sixty minutes and not wanting to push our luck, we promptly headed back over the bridge and home.

"Bill is leading Ratched on," I told Annelies when I dropped him off at home. He blushed, and we all laughed.

"Well, Bill," she said in her Swiss accent, "you made your bed, and have no one to blame but your own charming self." She taunted him, and we laughed again. They were crazy about each other.

For the next week, Bill and I would both lay on our respective couches unable to move, calling each other every day to compare side effects and keep each other's mood up. Going through cancer treatment with another patient is a very bonding and intimate experience.

You find yourself sharing thoughts and fears that you would never speak aloud to others.

As Bill and I shared our bizarre adventure together, we made it as entertaining as possible. We were chemo buddies. Though we were an unlikely pair, we got through the ordeal together—Dr. Bill, the convertible, the lectures, chemo, bets, Nurse Ratched, Shirley, Irish Coffee, and me. This was our therapy, physically and emotionally, and it was literally quite a ride.

When I finished reading this story, I looked up to see Dr. Marcus, who appeared transfixed.

"Did you really take Bill drinking at the bar after chemo?" He seemed dubious.

"Yes, of course," I responded. There was a moment of silence as he visualized chemo patients in a bar after treatment.

"Priceless!" he shouted through his laughter.

♀ ♀ ♀

A month or so later, I was asked if I would be willing to give an interview to the writing program's blog. I was honored and gave a written interview, which they titled "Inspirational Student Uses Writing to Heal." While I kept the details of my writing vague so no one could use my idea, I distinctly recall being very laudatory in my praise about Bonnie, her partner, and the writing program itself.

Interestingly, the final question of the interview relating to my screenplay was "What do you hope for?"

Ironically, in terms of subsequent events, my answer was this: "I hope that one of my now-famous Hollywood 'big shot' actors, producers, or directors, former students from Beverly, will hear about my film script, recognize its importance, and make it into a movie. Wouldn't that be the circle of life, and very, very cool?"

Under no circumstances, however, was I giving consent for it to be used without my permission. That article appeared in January of the following year. I didn't hear back from anyone about any of it, which was a bit disappointing.

Around that same time, I was encouraged by someone else, I can't remember whom, to submit my screenplay to the program's Screenplay Competition. For the time being, by entering the contest I was just hoping to get some constructive criticism, which was promised to the winners, though I never expected to win. It was too strange a topic.

By then I was barely able to think clearly, let alone type, due to all the meds I was on. Alice, a drama friend, came to my rescue. Intimately familiar with scripts, she gladly typed the rest of the screenplay while I dictated it to her. In the end, I knew that when I was stronger, and after taking a much-needed break, I would rework it to my satisfaction.

With that in mind, I phoned the person in charge of the competition from my home in Marin, to answer a couple of questions for me. At the last minute, I also asked about infringement issues. He seemed flabbergasted that I would even ask, and unequivocally told me that infringement issues were unheard of in the program, but if I was concerned that I should get a copyright. I then reassured myself because I had not one but two, from both Library of Congress and Writer's Guild West. I faxed him my script but, as requested, I also mailed a hard copy to meet the deadline.

With that done, although it was still a work-in-progress, I thought I was onto something important, completely unique, and which could be of help to others navigating the crazy world of cancer. When finished, I would reach out to see about getting it produced.

9

Friends

Not long after, I bumped into an old friend, Jill, having lunch at a restaurant. She ordered Chinese chicken salad. I just had a cappuccino. I was never hungry, but it's always good to get out whenever possible.

We talked about our kids who grew up together, what she was up to these days, and I mentioned my writing and shared the positive feedback I was getting from the teachers. She asked what I was writing about, and I boldly admitted, "cancer."

Her eyes opened wide; she seemed floored, and looked at me like I was completely out of my mind.

"Why would you want to write about that? Isn't it bad enough that you have to live it?" She blurted it out without any regard to my feelings.

I was speechless and really didn't know how to answer her.

"Have you ever read Anne Frank's diary?" I asked. Jill

wasn't Jewish, but most people I knew were completely aware of Anne Frank and her family's brave struggle hiding from the Nazis.

"No, but I've heard about it, the Jewish girl?"

"Right." I began carefully. "She was only thirteen years old when her family went into hiding from the Nazis for a couple of years in a hidden attic in Amsterdam. She wrote in a diary the entire time she was in hiding, and after a couple of years somebody betrayed them and her whole family was sent to Auschwitz. Anne died in the concentration camp. After the war, her book was discovered and became a testimony to the human spirit."

"That's depressing," she replied.

I was devastated that she couldn't see the connection and I continued nevertheless, but I don't know why I bothered.

"I've been reading this book called *Man's Search for Meaning*." I began to explain Dr. Frankl's book and the psychiatrist's powerful use of Nietzsche's aphorism: "He who has a why to live for can bear almost any how." The line had haunted me for years and kept coming back to me in my darkest hours like a healing song lyric.

"Huh?" Her eyes began to glaze over.

"If I were you, I would just want to have fun," she replied. "But, whatever, I mean if it makes you happy..."

"It's not really about happiness," I replied.

"Well, if you're asking me, you just need to get over it."

"Huh?" I asked. "Did you just say get over it?" I was flabbergasted. "You're joking, right?"

"No, I'm not," she said.

"Are we talking about the same thing, incurable cancer? You want me to just get over it? That's what my writing is helping with. You don't understand how much I've been through. It's like playing Russian Roulette every month."

She shrugged, and I felt like the wind was knocked out of me.

It had, by now, been years of nonstop chemos, hormone therapies, surgeries, clinical trials, and multiple rounds of radiation.

"Look...I'm just being honest with you...it's depressing. Shouldn't you just try to focus on something positive?"

"Living is positive! Surviving is positive!"

"I'm just sayin'..."

"Just sayin'."

God, I was beginning to hate that phrase, although I too was guilty of having used it from time to time in casual conversation. To my ears, it had become the ultimate justification. You could say whatever you wanted to anyone without any sense of guilt as long as you add those three words.

I was dumbfounded. Did people really feel this way? I knew this conversation was already over and I needed to escape. I felt as if I were suffocating. I pretended to glance at my watch and made up an excuse to leave.

"Well, thanks for your perspective. Gosh, I'm late. I have to go." We said goodbye, and that was the last time I ever saw Jill.

But instead, I sat in the car ruminating about the conversation, realizing how lonely it made me feel, and how it vaporized my self-esteem. Is this what friends are for? I thought.

I wanted my life to have meaning and understanding, to give something back to the world. I truly hoped to make someone else's challenging journey with cancer, or for that matter anything else that was truly difficult, a little easier by letting them know that they were not alone. I now understood that where there is life, there truly is hope.

I also realized that the world was changing. The wonderful advent of the Internet made things infinitely better on many levels. But at the same, it was pulling people apart. We could access almost anything with the push of a button, which made us accustomed to immediate gratification. As the late actress/writer Carrie Fisher once cracked about life in the fast lane, "Instant gratification takes too long."

Cells phones, as convenient as they are, were becoming an intrusion in life and a total disruption to relationships. Getting through dinner or a conversation without the interference of an incoming phone call had become almost impossible. People didn't even talk to each other that much anymore either, avoiding direct contact by texting instead.

I remembered walking into the living room one day while my kids and their friends sat playing a game of Scrabble on their respective laptops rather than on the beautiful wooden Scrabble set that sat directly in front of them in the middle of the coffee table.

I felt in my heart that the world was coming unglued, just when I needed the security and stability I had grown up with. This new world order left people like me feeling distanced from those we loved, and very much alone. I sadly began to realize that a lot of people felt the way Jill did.

ℨ ℨ ℨ

The next time I saw Dr. Marcus, I mentioned my depressing encounter with Jill. He thought for a few moments and then said, "So what do you think of discussing a new approach with people?"

I swear to God, I had no idea what he was talking about. To me, the word "approach" sounded sterile.

"'Approach'? What does that mean?"

"Let me ask you first, have you spoken honestly with

your kids yet about your prognosis."

"You mean the talk? No, not yet. I keep putting it off, and I don't know what to say."

My eyes began to well up with tears again, and I reached for the box of Kleenex on the table in front of me.

"Why do you think you do that?" he asked.

"Do what?"

"I'm wondering why you always reach for the Kleenex that's furthest from you when there's always a box next to your foot?"

"What? Where? I guess it's just not in my line of vision. I forgot it was there."

"Or maybe you are searching for comfort that is far away?"

At first his comment seemed ridiculous to me, but the more I thought about it the more I realized that he was right. I was searching for the comfort from those twenty people in the elevators in that Santa Monica hospital, all those many years ago.

I still had no idea as to what he meant by "approach," however, but as Emily in Our Town finds, you can't go back.

I understood that we have to keep putting one foot in front of the other. Forward is the only direction God gave us.

❧ ❧ ❧

A few days later, Dr. Bill and I went to our regular chemo races. We walked in expecting to see our friend Shirley, who always scheduled her appointments the same days as ours. But her chair was empty, and I felt a sudden hollowness in the pit of my stomach.

"Where's Shirley?" Dr. Bill asked.

One of the nurses came over and quietly explained to us that, of all things, her heart had given out and she was gone. We were shocked and deeply saddened, and neither of us was in the mood for chemo races that day. I reminded Dr. Bill of the time that he and Shirley surprised me at home one afternoon to give me a boost. It was very special.

Nevertheless, we still went to the Buena Vista afterward, but this time, it was to toast our "drippy friend." We were both very silent for the ride home, and the irony that she died out of the blue and from something completely unrelated to cancer was not lost on either of us.

Several months later, my buddy, Dr. Bill, passed away. Though he was in his eighties, I was heartbroken. He was a friend, a gentleman, and a great intellect. Moreover, I had also lost the last of my chemo buddies, and was afraid for my future as well. By now I had also lost a number of other good friends from cancer and was all too familiar with the insidious pain and heartbreak this disease had not only caused them, but all their families as well. In addition, I began to feel what some call "survivor's guilt."

As I waited for Dr. Grant the following day, I picked up my chart and noticed that three of the four happy faces had been crossed off. It caught me off guard, and I felt my heart race. I was weak, thin, and getting worse from another clinical trial I was on. He came into the room and gave me a hug.

"How are you doing?" he asked.

"I lost three of my four happy faces. Wow! That's a lot."

"You know, Nancy, our goal has always been to give you the best 'quality of life.'" Those words were still a recurring theme with every doctor, and always would be for me.

He reached for my arm to clean it with alcohol.

"Wait! I'm so tired of everything...being dripped, drugged, scanned and rescanned to death, no pun intended. You know, I've actually started enjoying Berry Smoothy, the new flavor of barium. It's the highlight of my month."

He chuckled and added, "I understand."

"When you have an incurable disease and no prospect of getting better...and if the side effects of the treatment...make you feel worse than the symptoms of the disease...isn't that a good time...to stop?"

He stopped rubbing my arm and took my hand in his.

"Possibly. But part of it depends on how many different treatments you've been on. And, frankly you've been on...a lot. What you haven't been on will only make you feel...sicker. Since we can't cure you, this is all about—"

"I know—quality of life."

There was a long pause.

"Maybe it's a good time to take a break," he said. I thought about his suggestion.

"A break...I like that idea."

"It's always been your choice."

"My choice. Then...I want to stop treatment...for now. Is that okay?"

"In that case, I'll give you back your arm."

"Are you mad at me?"

"Of course not," he said, letting out a long sigh.

"Are you disappointed?"

"Disappointed yes, but never in you. In myself, in what we docs can and can't do. You know this has always has been about you, and how you feel."

"Please don't feel disappointed," I told him. "You have been terrific, kind, professional, understanding, and a good friend."

He smiled.

"But...what do I tell my kids?" I asked hesitantly. "I'm afraid they won't understand."

As I waited for the doctor's answer, a warm feeling swept over me. I realized my first thoughts and concerns weren't about me. My heart and mind immediately went to my children. I felt my eyes moisten and my sense of resolve strengthened.

"Why don't you just tell them we decided you need a break?" he said, as if from far away. "Maybe they'll surprise you."

Coming back to my senses, I answered, "I like this idea…nothing permanent…a break!"

"Okay, then, let's talk about pain meds."

A shiver ran through me the minute he uttered the words pain meds. I hated taking them. They made me sicker, more tired, and gave me migraines.

"I can't tolerate those meds. I'm better off with just ibuprofen and marijuana."

"Deal. We will find another treatment, I promise," he said.

"Can I ask you one more question?" I asked timidly.

"Shoot."

"Do many husbands leave their wives under… circumstances like these?" I was desperate to know.

"Once in a while. I can't imagine the pain this is causing you, Nancy. I'm so sorry. If it helps, there are people who just can't cope. Fight or flight. And, you can't let him drag you down. You need your strength to fight the cancer." He gave me a long hug when I left. I deeply appreciated his honest and caring manner. I told him I was going back to L.A., for a while, but that I would be back, and that Dr. Chap would follow me while I was there.

Later in the day, I was home, trying to rest and collect my thoughts, when the phone rang. It was my good friend Sheryl again, who wanted to know about my doctor's appointment. I told her about having to quit the treatment for the time being, but that we hoped a new treatment would become available. I told her we could have coffee the following day.

That evening my pent-up anxiety drove me to start cleaning. Cleaning always made me feel better, and vacuuming was my favorite. There was something so therapeutic in seeing debris get instantaneously sucked away. I wanted to vacuum my life. More importantly, I was thinking about what to tell my kids about quitting treatment.

"Mom, where are you?" Dina said, calling for me.

"I'm in the closet."

"Mother. What are you doing?"

"I am...nesting," I told her.

"Huh? You're what?" I turned off the vacuum.

"Nesting. It's what women do," I repeated.

"Okay, stop. I have no idea what you're talking about."

"That's because you don't nest yet," I explained.

"Are you okay?" she asked.

Dina sat on the floor next to me. She could never imagine how much I loved her. But now I was feeling broken for her because of the news I had to share. How would she cope with the possible loss of her mother? Could she deal with it? I realized that there were so many things that I hadn't yet discussed with her. Maybe this was a good place to start "The Talk," which I had been too terrified to discuss with my kids.

"Look, women are like birds. They need to keep their home and family organized. It's how women control life when it's getting out of control. And my life is feeling very much out of control right now."

"What? I'm a bird with a nest?"

I burst out laughing and gave her a hug.

"It's not like telling you how babies are born. It's the kind of thing that one day you would say to me, 'I think something's wrong with me because I just spent two hours cleaning the refrigerator.' And, I would tell you that it's normal. And, you would say OK, and that would be the end of it. I'm just realizing there are a lot of things I want to tell you about, and you must have so very many questions."

I could no longer speak, what I had to say felt so unspeakable.

"Mom!" Jake yelled from the living room, interrupting our conversation. "You have some guests!"

"Who is it?" I yelled back.

"I'm not sure?" he yelled back. "You better come."

I wasn't expecting anyone, and couldn't imagine who would be visiting me at this late hour. But I was relieved not to have to finish that conversation. I couldn't. I walked over to the door and opened it.

My jaw dropped to the floor and my eyes welled with tears. Standing before me was a large group of my closest friends, my own personal female Superheroes in full regalia. To my surprise and without exception, they had all risen to the occasion and gathered on the street in front of my house, where they had changed into costumes. All to cheer me up! I was overjoyed. They were giddy to be in their Superhero costumes again, as well.

It was then and there that I realized that Superheroes really do exist; they're called "friends."

𝑋 𝑋 𝑋

Over the years, I had continued to make myself available for coaching actors/students I had previously worked with. I had directed my daughter's friend Alice as Emily in *Our Town*. She was enormously talented, and I loved working with her, especially on that play, my favorite.

Now she needed some "urgent" help with the character for her college audition, and asked if she could come over. "Of course!" I told her.

Alice arrived at the front door and Dina greeted her.

"Hi, Alice. God, love the hair," she said. As he often did, Jake came out of the kitchen, smiling, proudly carrying a plate of food.

"Hey, Alice," he said flirtatiously. "I heard you turned eighteen. Does that mean you'll go out with me now?"

Dina snapped at him, "Stop hitting on my friends."

"It's OK," Alice laughed. "He made me promise one date when I turned eighteen." She whispered to Dina. "Anyway, he's kind of cute."

"Hey, Mom. Can we watch?" Jake asked.

"It's up to Alice."

"Well, an audience would sort of help."

We all walked out to the studio together. I noticed Jake tried to nonchalantly put his arm on Alice's shoulder, but she shrugged it off. He tried again a few minutes later, and succeeded. I flipped on the studio spotlight in my now-smaller studio. My kids sat in the back where it was dark.

"Let's warm up, Alice." She knew the drill. She took a deep-cleansing breath and rolled her neck. Then she stretched and shook her arms.

I began to walk her through the scene, one of my favorite activities in life.

"Let's take a walk down Main Street," I began. "No words this time. Just the feelings. It's the early 1900s. We have to see, hear, touch, and smell everything. Start with the clocks ticking, and let me know when you hear them."

Slowly, my immensely talented and very sensitive daughter, who often worked with me when I directed, was riveted to this scene.

"I hear them," Alice said.

"What do they sound like?" I prodded.

"Big old grandfather clocks chiming."

"Do you see the flowers? Where are they? What kind?" I asked.

She pointed and said, "Right there. And there too. They're big...beautiful...sunflowers."

I could see her seeing what I was pointing out. My heart was filled with joy as I saw my visualization exercise actually working. God, I love directing!

"Excellent," I encouraged her. "Now the coffee, smell the coffee. You love all these things." I coached her the way I coached everyone, slowly and hypnotically. Alice became caught up in all of it.

"Now...I want you to see the people you love, your mother and father. What do they look like?

"So wonderful and young."

"Reach out to touch them...but you can't...feel as they pass through your fingers like a cloud. Your heart is breaking." Alice began to cry.

"And now you're angry...they can't hear you....you call out to them and make them listen!"

"Mother! Father!" She yells at them.

Jake put his sandwich on the chair, and Dina leaned in.

"They don't hear you…now slowly turn and start to walk away." She does. "The pain is unbearable because you can't get them back."

"Stop. Hold it. Now slowly look back at them one more time. See all of it, everything. Take one good long, last look at the world." Alice turned to her imaginary parents, and tears were streaming down her face.

"Turn back to the stage manager and ask him the question you need to know."

"They don't understand how precious life is…every minute."

Dina quietly dissolved into tears as she suddenly made the connection to our lives. Jake leaned over and put his arm around her. He cradled her as she unleashed her heart. I started to walk over to comfort them, but Jake raised his hand to stop me as if to say, "I've got this, Mom."

The next time I saw Dr. Marcus he asked me how "The Talk" went with my kids.

"Thornton Wilder laid the groundwork for me."

"How's that?" he asked. I told him about the *Our Town* rehearsal. I thought I saw sadness in his eyes that I hadn't seen before. He paraphrased Ray Carver's notable poetic question, which he posed at the end of his own life, "Did you get what you wanted out of life?"

"Absolutely," I responded. I remind myself of that every day. I've had a great life."

And it had been, despite the pain of these last years. How many people get to do the work they love? Have children? I've been blessed.

I also told him that I was thinking of going back to L.A. for radiation, but that I would keep in touch, and he wished me well.

10

Three for Three

In 2009, my family was struck with more horrific news. My younger brother by five years, Mike, was diagnosed with a different but deadly form of cancer called Liposarcoma. I was happy that I had decided to go back to Los Angeles, in part, to be closer to him. I also realized how much I needed a break from Marin and all the memories of recent times. I moved to Westwood, and continued to finish the classes towards my screen-writing credential.

I always knew that I was in great hands with Dr. Chap, as with my other doctors. I checked in with her regularly throughout the years. I adored her, and she considered me a special patient and was amazed by my ongoing survival. I continued with my never-ending quarterly scans and nonstop treatments. She remains a champion to me and always continues to inspire me.

Mike and I had always been very close, and I looked

after him a lot when he was young due to our mother's Multiple Sclerosis. I also tried as much as possible to be there for him when he was older, as well as his two boys who lived with him. At the time, he was a single working dad. My little brother, who was always my buddy, was now fighting for his life too. It tore me apart.

Mike was being treated by doctors from a small, unknown practice, who I felt were not adequate for the severity of this illness. I had learned from my own experience to find the best possible doctors. I found two top-notch doctors through people I had met while volunteering at UCLA, and insisted that my brother see them. His girlfriend, who many years later became his wife, also found a new doctor to join his medical team. He switched doctors and hospitals, and although it was a terrible ordeal—a year of numerous surgeries, treatments, and complications—they saved his life.

Not long after that, the final shoe dropped.

Our sister, Lara, had joined a Breast Cancer Sister Study back east, to be monitored closely because of my own breast cancer. Suddenly and horrifically, she too was diagnosed with cancer. It was unfathomable that all three of us had cancer. There was no family history for what the three of us had.

"I can't believe this, Lara, I'm so sorry."

Then, I went quiet. For the first time in my life, I was totally at a loss for what to say. "Welcome to the club" just wasn't funny in the least so I didn't say it, but it was clear to us that we had all become members of the dreaded club that no one wishes to be part of. It was soul crushing and a living nightmare.

"It's okay, Nan, as strange as it may sound I've been expecting this news since you and Mike were diagnosed."

That was really all there was for her to say. Fortunately, hers was a small Stage 1 tumor that was easily removed, and hopefully that would be the end of it for her.

Our parents had been smokers and, of course, we had been exposed to second-hand smoke as kids. But, so were countless other kids of the '50s and '60s. Was that the reason? We all had worked for our dad as kids. Had we had been unknowingly exposed to dangerous cleaning chemicals. Was that the reason? We were of Ashkenazi descent, a population of Jews who come from Eastern Europe and have a higher incidence of breast cancer. Was that the reason?

Lara and I were both tested for the BRCA genes, the same tests that Angelina Jolie took and so bravely spoke about, but our BRCA gene test results were negative. Anyway, that wouldn't have explained Mike's illness. It was all enormously scary and heart-wrenching. We were at an utter loss how to grasp this, let alone explain this triple whammy to our kids. I enrolled my daughter in a high-risk monitoring program, which will follow her for life.

But most importantly and miraculously, we were all surviving. We had so much to be thankful for.

ℜℜℜ

One night, while I was sitting in a restaurant around the corner from my apartment having a rare glass of wine, I was thinking about the sudden twist of fate that had beset my sister and brother. I started thinking about many years earlier, the day before our dad was going in for major surgery for the second time. I took my baby, Jake, to his house. When Jake and I arrived, Dad was eagerly waiting outside for us with a huge smile and his trademark, "HEY, BUDDY!" Dad was in his element. Of all the things he had ever been in his life, he was best at being a grandpa.

I ran out to the pool just in time to see my dad, a tall man of good physique, dive off the board into the pool. He looked like a whale as he swam across the bottom of the pool to the other side and back again, never surfacing for a breath.

I jumped in the pool, and waited at the edge of the diving board with my dad to catch Jake, who was holding Mom's hand. Dad yelled.

"Come on, buddy, one, two, three—jump!"

On three, Jake jumped into the pool. As soon as he surfaced, he blinked the water from his eyes and, mad with excitement, he shouted, "Again!" We replayed the event over and over, each and every detail, the squealing, the counting, the jumping, the blinking, and "Again!" We shouted and clapped every time.

Suddenly, Dad got out of the pool, dried himself quickly, and announced that he had to go out. I couldn't imagine what on earth could be so important that he would leave this absolutely perfect playdate.

"He'll be right back," I said, as Jake began to cry.

As promised, my dad returned twenty minutes later. I was stunned when I saw what he brought with him…an entire carload of pool toys. It was truly the kindest and most loving gesture I had ever seen. My father, who didn't know if he would be alive this same time tomorrow, took his precious little time to fill his swimming pool with toys for his cherished grandson. In the end, it was one of the most memorable and wonderful days of my life.

My heart was filled with an infusion of love, and the most peaceful thought floated into my mind: God, I love my son, my father, and my mother. At the moment the world was so radiant, I wanted to freeze time, and hoped that tomorrow wouldn't be the end of these glorious days.

ℜ ℜ ℜ

Six months after my dad's surgery, my brother was getting married. It too was another bittersweet experience with my dad. Although he had barely survived his surgery, which had pushed him closer and closer to death, any semblance of "quality of life" had been destroyed.

Watching what he had to endure, I vowed after I was diagnosed that I would not allow that to happen to me.

My dad had always been a good dancer, and he was delighted when the DJ played Frank Sinatra's version of the song "Chicago," our hometown song. I helped him to his feet and we shuffled out onto the dance floor, but he was now too frail and weak. So we just swayed back and forth on the dance floor taking in the joy of this moment, relishing the fact we could celebrate Mike's wedding.

"I have one more thing to look forward to," he said as he glanced down at my seven-month-pregnant, swollen belly. "And then I'm ready to meet my maker."

There was no sorrow in his voice. He was happy and content with his life, the family he had raised, and he always adored my mom. He was also thrilled to be here this day to see his only son get married.

I thought back also to my grandpa, who had struggled so hard to relearn how to walk with his wooden legs so that he could dance at his grandson's wedding. These two men had become towering symbols of strength and courage to me, and I was determined to follow their lead. They are inspirations to me, even now, decades later, and I feel them, with all their strength, watching over all of us. I remain very happy for that.

My grandfather Marvin is in the front row 1961.

On the left is my dad and I (7 months pregnant at my
brother's wedding 1986). Both men were gravely ill at
the time but their goal was to dance at their grandson's
and son's weddings.

II

Life on the Tube

It was now the spring of 2010, six months after I serendipitously moved back to Los Angeles. As I stepped off the curb onto busy Wilshire Blvd. with my dog, Allie, I was almost struck by a big blue transit bus that seemed to careen out of nowhere. I instinctively jumped back to safety, but was stunned at the sight of an enormous advertisement on the side of the bus as it passed by me. A certain famous actress, I'll call her "Candy," was pictured lounging in her bathing suit on a beach. Next to her was a large hourglass that was— clearly symbolically—running out of sand.

Coincidentally, earlier that morning when I was volunteering at the cancer center, I heard some patients talking about a new TV "cancer comedy" starring Candy. Some patients were uncomfortable at the thought of a cancer comedy, while others felt the idea was long overdue. I was stunned to hear that a show about cancer was airing simultaneous to the cancer screenplay that I was still polishing. However, I felt certain that whatever the show was it had to be very different than mine, with all its unique aspects. So, I just listened intently and made a mental note to check it out when I got home.

The bus advertisements were part of a massive ad campaign announcing the upcoming premiere of this new TV series. Over the years I had seen countless ad campaigns for movies and television series on buses, which are commonplace in L.A. Just then, a second bus zoomed by, with Candy now depicted in a swimming pool. At that moment a shudder ran through my entire body as the parallels to my life and my screenplay began haunting me.

Each day more and more buses continued to pass by my apartment every few minutes. Eventually, I tried to avert my eyes and ignore them, but I already instinctively began to dislike them, which made me determined to find out exactly what kind of cancer show this was. For the next two months, I scoured the Internet, but couldn't find much information about it.

Finally, my curiosity got the better of me, and on August 16, 2010, I tuned in to watch the pilot episode of the show. I wasn't alone. The premiere apparently drew the giant cable company's largest ever opening audience as of that date.

However and to my delight, the first person who appeared in the show was an actor I'll call "Lou," who happened to be my *former acting student* from Beverly Hills High. It was commonplace for me to see my former students in TV shows or films, and the recognition always brought a smile to my face. Lou was an immensely gifted black actor whom I'd had the pleasure of directing when he played Ace Stamper for me in *Splendor in the Grass*. A terrific character actor, the late Pat Hingle, had played that role in the Oscar-winning 1961 film written by William Inge and directed by Elia Kazan. It also starred Natalie Wood, and introduced for the very first time one of my all-time favorite heartthrobs, Warren Beatty.

Still smiling, I turned my attention back to the show and took a special interest in Lou, hoping that he had a good recurring role on this show. He certainly deserved it, I thought. However, when his character turned out to be a swimming pool contractor who was hired to build a *swimming pool for cancer-stricken* Candy, I froze.

"Yikes, what a coincidence," I thought.

Collecting myself and refocusing on the show, I was soon hit by yet another extraordinary coincidence when Candy's husband rode up to the house on a Vespa. Though part of me was still fixated on Lou and the swimming pool, the appearance of the *Vespa* unnerved me because I had ridden one for many years and also wrote about it in my screenplay.

"I don't believe this," I said aloud, jumping out of my chair.

Then, Candy's husband revealed that the two of them had *separated*, at which point I was mortified by yet another painful similarity to my life and writing.

"What the hell!" I shouted, as my dog ran to me.

I counted out the coincidences on my now trembling hands—one, two, three...*four* extraordinary coincidences to my life and screenplay, and all within the first few minutes.

Everything felt utterly surreal, and unlike anything I had ever experienced before. My heart raced while my mind worked in slow motion, like it does when you are in the midst of a car accident. What were the chances of all of this simply being simply a coincidence—one in a zillion?

I began pacing up and back, as the next scene sent me reeling. Candy now sat in a medical gown in her *charming young male doctor's* office. Her robe was loosely open and her breasts were exposed enough so that she was *joking about her lack of modesty,* like I had. Instinctively, I strained to see if her belt was lying uncooperatively on the floor like mine.

Feeling sucker-punched by *now six* coincidences, my heart pounded at an alarming rate, as if I was having a heart attack. My legs gave way, and I stumbled backwards over the ottoman onto the sofa, and then it hit me like a ton of bricks.

I know this story. I'm living proof of it. I am this story!

I turned and shouted at the TV. "Lou—don't build that damn pool! It's me—Nancy!" Just then my new ringtone, "I Will Survive!", called to me. It was Lara, my sister.

"Are you watching that show?"

"Yes…"

"This is all the same stuff you wrote about!"

"Yes," I said, still utterly flabbergasted.

"Take notes! I'm taking notes, too! I'll call you back in a while."

As soon as I hung up, "I Will Survive!" rang on my phone again and again and again. Family and friends, who also obviously recognized my life in the show and knew I had been writing about it, were calling to congratulate me on getting my screenplay produced. *Ouch!* That really hurt. It seemed to be my story, but not my exact words.

"You don't understand; it's not my exact script," I told them. They were as confused as I was. I quickly hung up the phone so I could continue watching and scribbling notes on a paper towel. There was no time to search for paper.

I sat there dumbfounded for I don't know how long, until Lara called back later. She was as upset as I was because she knew practically every word of my script. I had previously read many scenes to her over the phone and emailed her some others to read. Moreover, in addition to my screenplay, she was intimately aware of every detail of my life, from which it had been drawn.

"You know, Nancy, you might expect to find some of these things in a story about cancer…"

"*Scènes à faire*," I told her in my best French accent, which is terrible.

"Huh? What does that mean?"

"Scenes you might expect to see, given the topic."

"But *all* of these? This is outrageous!" She was distraught for me.

"*Scènes à* UN-*faire!*" The play on words did not amuse her.

"This isn't funny. You've worked really hard on all this. How did this happen?" She was now outraged, and I was really crying inside. She knew I had spent years and precious ergs of energy purging everything I had gone through in my writing. Bam! It evaporated in this instant.

I couldn't sleep the night of premiere. The prospect of the show became a living nightmare. Finally at 2 a.m., unable to close my eyes, I got out of bed and lugged out a huge box of all my screenplay stuff. Writing projects are one of the few things I save anymore, and I had been compulsive about saving every draft I had written in my screenwriting classes.

I carefully spread everything out on the floor, which took up the entire living room and overflowed into the dining room. Then I turned on the computer and printed out the complete email index of roughly 700 assignments, amounting to hundreds of pages, which I had dutifully sent to my teachers, as well as every one of the their responses back to me.

By the time the first episode had ended, it seemed crystal clear to me that someone in the writer's program had given away my screenplay. But who? As a teacher, I always felt that the bond between a teacher and student was sacrosanct.

As the weeks went by, Lara and I continued watching the program, which became an absolutely insufferable experience, while adding to our ongoing and ever growing list of similarities to my screenplay.

Having taught creative writing I was very familiar with the creation of characters, conflicts, relationships, themes, symbolic imagery, metaphors, and all the rest of the other creative expressive elements. The significance of all these similarities to my screenplay was undeniable, and excruciating for me.

After I finished laying out all of my work, I began the painstaking work of placing every class assignment and every draft of my script in strict chronological order. The entire floor, dining table, refrigerator door, and walls were plastered and pinned up with scenes from my screenplay. I tried to think back, but four years was a long time and many painful experiences ago. The sheer amount of work that I had put into my script was staggering. Moreover, I had written everything while on chemo and other treatments.

As the series unfolded, episode after painful episode, I felt as if I were beginning to lose my mind. My apartment was cluttered with all the paper, lists, computer printouts, and scenes. Hopscotching over all of it, I went outside to take a break, and of course, there were all the freaking blue buses. One after the other after the other, as if they were thumbing their noses at me. It got to the point that every time another blue bus passed by, I felt as if it were driving right over my heart, which was now lying somewhere in the middle of bumper-to-bumper Wilshire Boulevard.

Eventually, Allie began sensing that I needed to avoid the buses altogether, as the mere sight of them was making me sick to my stomach. She began pulling me towards the alley instead. My dog was amazingly in tune with me, and had actually scented out my last bout of bone cancer, alerting me by licking my shoulder for months. The day I had radiation to my shoulder, she stopped doing it. God, I love that dog!

So, Allie and I resorted to the humiliating act of leaving my apartment building through the back door and cutting down the alley, so I wouldn't have to see the endless parade of blue buses anymore. The entire scenario was hilariously pathetic, and reminded me of something you might see in a Woody Allen film.

The more I thought about it—and by now I was consumed by it—the more I became sickened at the prospect that I had wasted these precious last few years of my life by writing something that I now could only throw in the trash. It had all become completely pointless and irrelevant! But there was something much worse than that as well.

If I continued writing, others would now assume that I merely copied someone else's work, which was utterly untrue and painfully ironic. I had struggled and lived through, in one way or another, everything I had written.

Nevertheless, I continued to comb through countless pages of scripts, notes, letters, and emails. I desperately tried to see if there was anything at all that I might be able to salvage from my work that would still be original, new, and of interest to anyone on this planet. There wasn't much left. And, my hopes for selling my screenplay and, more importantly, *using it as a springboard to help other real cancer patients*, evaporated.

I had also invested precious time and considerable money building a nonprofit, LivingBeyondStatistics.org. A wonderful former student, actress Joely Fisher (also the sister of the late Carrie), and Joely's extraordinary notable friends had made a fabulous video for my website. Any form of credit that the TV show was a derivational work or adapted from my personal screenplay would have given my non-profit formidable legs on which to stand. Without it made getting the non-profit off the ground much more difficult. Furthermore, without any payment for my screenplay, I decided I could no longer afford to pour any money into the website as I selfishly needed to conserve all of my finances for my cancer care. The site *was evaporating right before my very eyes*. I had to do something to salvage my life and my vision.

Eventually, I found the title page and log line of my screenplay. I reread every single page, partly to prove to myself I wasn't crazy and that I had indeed written exactly what I thought I had written. Sure enough, the list of similarities substantiated my suspicions.

"Quality of Life
A dramedy about love, laughter, and cancer
by
Nancy Radin

"When a vibrant California teacher and mother of teens is suddenly diagnosed with Stage 4 cancer, she must overcome the shock of the death sentence, complications of a cancer group, her children's conflicted reactions—and her husband's surprise walk-out—as she sets out to live the last of her life on her own terms."

Against all the odds, I had struggled, beyond on anyone's comprehension, to live through and write my screenplay, which emanated from a very deep place of heartfelt and hard-earned insight and pain. That was especially so when it came to finding humor in the darkness, my personal coping mechanism and survival technique. I had been devastated these last years not only for my marriage, my siblings, and myself, but mostly for my children, who had experienced one catastrophe after another.

For four precious years, I had invested my heart and bared my soul to tell the truth about my life in a screenplay to help other cancer patients and individuals who also felt overwhelmed by their challenges. I wanted to let them know that they are not alone. It had, without question, been the most excruciating decade of my life, and I had written about all of it.

Despite the fact that I was somehow inexplicably beating the odds, I now felt myself crumbling inside from the weight of it all. It was clear to me that I had to get back on top of my life, and fighting for my screenplay became part of my strategy for doing exactly that. It was critical that whatever the outcome, I had to stand up for myself, as I always have done.

Furthermore, I have always taught my children to stand up for themselves, though I was now pitifully hiding from the blue buses right in front of my building.

Finding dark humor, as my grandfather and mother had always done, was the only way for me to make my pain more tolerable. With all the cancer in my family the last few years, I'd also learned to have a healthy respect for the insidious disease, the misery and death it can wreak. Now, since my diagnosis and that of my siblings, as well as other friends and loved ones who had suffered from and died from cancer, with each death the hole in my heart grew bigger.

However, and for the time being, I decided that I had to give the show's creator the benefit of the doubt. I told myself that she too must have suffered terribly in her cancer ordeal to be able to write this from a sympathetic viewpoint. So again I began researching the show on the Internet, to see what kind of cancer the creator suffered from and how she had come up with so many apparent similarities to my work. In fact, I actually began to feel sorry for her and her personal tragedy in dealing with her cancer.

That is...until I learned *that she never even had cancer*! Wow! The whole thing was inauthentic and felt completely sacrilegious, although I read that the creator had stated that it was "real," whatever that meant?

Still unable to completely wrap my head around this, I thought for a few moments and wondered. Maybe there was a real honest-to-goodness clairvoyance thing going on, like when the rabbi serendipitously turned up in my room at the hospital?

Perhaps I was truly getting some kind of telepathic message, though I had never ever considered myself to be even remotely telepathic. In light of this bizarre sur-realism, anything was possible. Right? And, what if the message was that I really needed to reach out to her, or them, whoever they were, to help them? I began to feel that as a surviving cancer patient, I was morally obligated to assist them.

With that in mind, and feeling compelled to reach out, I actually envisioned that the show's writing team was hoping to hear from me, a writer who was surviving (now eight years) from the same disease. I told myself that they would not only be happy to hear from me, but that they were literally waiting for me to contact them.

So, I contacted the cable production company, which by some divine intervention was located directly across the street from where I lived, reinforcing the notion of telepathy. I left my name and number and was anxious to hear back, which I assumed would be only a matter of hours or a couple of days at most. I waited patiently. But...they *never* returned my call. And, only much later did it occur to me that I was probably the ONE person on the entire planet whom they *never ever* wanted to hear from.

After that, I continued digging, and the more digging I did the more revealing quotes about the series I found, ranging from the *Los Angeles Times* blog to the Writer's Guild. I tacked them all up on the cork on my refrigerator so I could study them and try to make some sense of them.

From the wga.org website I learned that the creator recounted her initial meeting with one of the producers who told her: *"It's time for a cancer comedy,"* and she said the producer had sent her *"articles and funny perspectives on cancer."*

Having never heard back from them, I began to wonder whose articles and funny perspectives they were, and had no choice but to strongly suspect they were mine.

Then there was this from the creator on how she came up with the concept for the show. On the thewrap.com I read: *"Then one day I looked at my new beautiful, perfect innocent baby and started crying... that was my way in."*

Geez, I'd had two beautiful babies of my own, eighteen months apart, both by Caesarian section—and I had Lupus. Yet, I never once thought about dying, that is, *until I actually got Stage 4 cancer.* It seemed incredulous to me that someone could claim having been inspired to create this series—an exploration of a fatal disease about death and dying—out of the joyous experience of having a healthy baby. Had someone whispered in her ear, "If you say having a baby inspired you, then *nobody* can ever doubt you?"

It made no sense, on any level, in any universe, including the strange universe of Hollywood.

When I mentioned these quotes to my doctors, they were appalled. The experience was becoming more freakish by the day, and was all so seemingly unreal I began to feel like a total fool.

Then I read in the *L.A. Times* blog that the now much-praised creator of the series "wrote fifteen pilots over nine years before she landed this deal."

On the Writer's Guild blog I read that she also admitted in light of the show's success that she had recently revamped the advice she gives to aspiring writers from the standard *"write what you know"* to *"write what you know even if it doesn't seem like you know what you know."*

"Fool me once, shame on you; fool me twice then shame on me," as the old proverb says. Was I being fooled or shamed or both? It certainly felt that way. Either way it was beyond disturbing and as if 'something was rotten in the state of Denmark,' as Shakespeare wrote in *Hamlet*.

The cumulative effect was like being in electric shock therapy, one horrible jolt after the other until I was in a complete state of shock and utterly fried.

More importantly, some credited the show for being the first to bring cancer to the forefront of our collective consciousness. Others raved about dealing with cancer with some degree of humor. It was truly unique and poignant and resonated with people. I was both proud and crushed at the same time.

While I was gratified on the grander scale that the attention the show received could help the greater cancer cause, the awards and the acclaim were for me salt in the wounds. I struggled to think of another example of a scripted series about this uniquely negative topic—cancer—becoming such an enormous success, garnering numerous awards, including Emmy, Golden Globe, and other prizes.

One day, I bumped into the writing program's director on the street, whom I had met on a number of occasions. She knew me because I was older than most of the other students, and also stood out from the crowd due to my mobility issues, which had become a huge problem for me.

I explained my dilemma, that I had invested almost four years and roughly six thousand dollars in the writing program. I discussed my suspicions over the recent TV series, the troubling pattern of similarities to my work, and the entire scenario, which felt incredibly surreal to me. I asked for her help, but was staggered by her response. She became very defensive and simply walked away from me, refusing to take any further calls or emails.

Not being one to give up, I then contacted the program manager who said, "In truth, dozens of people might have had access to your material," and referred me to the Writer's Guild for further help.

The trouble was that I *hadn't* shared my work with *dozens* of people, just the instructors and supposedly just the two competition judges. I was getting absolutely nowhere.

Finally, I contacted the dean, who also suggested I

contact the Writer's Guild, and said *"I can confirm that this is the process we have followed in similar cases."*

"Similar cases?"

I had specifically been told when I entered the contest that they *hadn't had this issue before*. This entire situation was beginning to feel like a James Patterson mystery novel.

I personally felt certain that there were only two ways anyone could have gained access to my script. The first possibility was that one of my teachers or someone in the writing program had given away my screenplay, which seemed the most obvious and likely.

The second possibility was that the creator was amazingly clairvoyant and had channeled into every fiber of my soul.

Neither scenario was acceptable!

Very distressed, my mind again turned to Dr. Frankl, and though the circumstances of his life in the camps were obviously much graver and more horrific than mine, I completely understood how he must have felt as he watched the only copy of his manuscript disappear in the concentration camp. He wrote, "I know what you will say: that I should be grateful to escape with my life, that should be all I can expect of fate. But I cannot help myself. I must keep this manuscript at all costs."

This was certainly not a fight I ever wanted to fight, nor could I have possibly imagined it in a million years.

But, it seemed I had no choice. I had to protect my baby, which the creator was also now referring to as her "lovechild." This was beginning to feel to me like a child custody battle. All artists I know are protective like that about their work.

I then made the decision to do the only thing I could now do. I had to find an attorney.

Eventually, I was put in touch with an attorney, Evan, who handled infringement issues. As I dialed the phone, I was filled with a cool certainty that it would be an open-and-shut case, a slam-dunk, and a sure thing. We felt that a reasonable jury would figure it all out, and "split the baby" as Solomon suggested in the Bible, and at least I might get a nice lock of hair.

After a lengthy description, he readily agreed to take my case. Shortly after, I send him a retainer, and he filed the papers. I felt much better and even began walking down Wilshire again, no longer afraid to encounter the buses. My self-esteem was back intact, and I was proud of myself. I could tell my dog was proud of me too, as she pranced down Wilshire Blvd. again with me.

In our communication we decided that Evan would depose the necessary parties, and subpoena all of the creator's work in development of the show including those "articles and funny perspectives" the producer sent to the creator. Then he would name parties in the lawsuit.

Out of the blue, in my attorney's car on the way home

from my long and disparaging deposition, he mentioned that the "creator" was adding a second floor to her house near the beach.

"What? How do you know that?" I asked him.

"I drove over there," he told me.

I wondered what and why in the world my attorney from the San Fernando Valley was doing near her house. I'm not a lawyer, but thought it was really inappropriate and very bizarre.

Not long afterward, he informed me that the case went to "summary judgment."

"What's 'summary judgment'?" I asked him, as he hadn't explained any of it to me.

"It means it's over," he said. "The case was dismissed. You lost!"

"How could I lose?" I asked. "We've just gotten started."

The only thing that I knew had happened was that I had given a long deposition, during which the defense attorney tried to portray me as a crazy and untalented woman. Once again, I felt betrayed.

At that time, my younger cousin, Maya, who is my daughter's age, had just finished her MBA in Colorado and wasn't sure what she wanted to do, so I offered her my extra bedroom. I told her she was welcome to stay with me in L.A. as long as she wanted. She stayed for about a year and until after she met her future husband, Paul. All the while, she was an absolute joy to have around, and it was great to have her support. Her parents, Dan and Meryl, visited frequently and accompanied me to my radiation appointments in L.A., for which I was ever grateful. Meryl's uncle was a prominent attorney, and was able to find me two other distinguished attorneys, brothers, who would appeal my case at a discounted rate, which I greatly appreciated.

These two wonderful gentlemen, whom I will always admire and adore, believed in my case and me, but cautioned that such cases are very difficult to win for two reasons. First were all the loopholes and flaws in infringement law, which can easily be skirted by maintaining the similarities but simply changing the language.

Second, they felt that the major companies involved in the cable series would do and spend whatever was necessary to win the case. I certainly didn't have the unlimited resources that they did.

Rodney explained to me that the whole copyright court feels more like *Upstairs, Downstairs*. I immediately understood that he was referring to the old British TV series (a precursor to *Downton Abbey*) that depicts the lives of the servants "downstairs" and their masters—the wealthy family—"upstairs." He continued that in copyright court the "celebrities are upstairs, and the unknown creatives are downstairs."

They further explained the two criteria we needed to prove our case. The first criterion was *"significant similarities"* between the show and my screenplay, which are comprised of expressive elements. This seemed like a no-brainer, as I whipped out a three-page list of similarities between my script and the TV show that my sister and I had come up with. The entire list was based on *authentic* experiences from my life, which included among others: a "dramedy" about a mother/teacher/wife/cancer patient, given an original eighteen-month prognosis, going through a marital separation from a husband who leaves and wants to have fun; centered around a therapeutic swimming pool; a friendly younger male oncologist; stressed teens; camping at the beach; an elderly white male and African-American heavyset support group; an altercation with police; a fancy sports car and a Vespa; a student with an urgent need, fixated on marijuana; an immodesty scene in the doctor's office; a close friend who dies unexpectedly; a cooking student at Le Cordon Bleu; a withdrawal of a large amount of money; dogs as significant characters; ending treatment on one's own terms; evaluating a doctor to his face; a bonfire in the backyard; and numerous others. I carefully selected all of these as expressive elements. They were real and from my life, not fantasy.

While the court recognized the similarities, they called them "abstract." They in no way appeared to be abstract to us.

One of the creator's scripts even called for a scene with an Indian medical marijuana salesperson. Upon my next visit to that particular place, I had found out that the person was actually Moroccan, but I never had time to change the script.

Nevertheless, the creator said that she had "never heard of, seen, or read any of" my screenplay or any work written by me. No explanation was ever given as to where or how these ideas came to her.

The second criterion for proving infringement was proving "access." This issue also seemed abundantly clear in the timeline we provided the court, which contained a fifteen-page index of my work (hundred of assignments) that I privately emailed to my teachers (all professional working L.A. writers) as well as their private email responses to me.

I felt I had to go forward and not give up. There was too much at stake for me to lose the years I had spent writing my screenplay. Plus, it was the only thing that could give legs to the nonprofit I was trying to build to help other cancer patients.

All in all, my long-term hope was to be allowed to present the case to a fair jury. We believed that they would find the series was a *derivational work based on my screenplay*, which it certainly seemed to be, and that I would receive some sort of professional credit. Without credit there was little I could do at this point in my life to jumpstart a new career in writing, and give legs to my non-profit to help other cancer patients. We also hoped for some amount of compensation out of fairness and decency, and which would greatly help my retirement and mounting medical bills.

My attorney, Rodney, argued that the documents my attorneys received from the defendant's attorneys and the writer's program were incomplete, or severely redacted to the point of being worthless.

In addition, the defendant's major piece of evidence, basically a short outline of a concept for a TV series, purported to prove that the show was a completely independent creation. However, the defense had this evidence *sealed* so the court could not read it. I didn't understand how "sealing" a document so the judges cannot see it could be possible, let alone legal, but it was.

This outline of the TV show existed prior to my screenplay, but had little to do with the story line, characters, relationships, or other elements that my screenplay contained. There was no forty-something woman, no married mother, no teens, no marital separation, no charming younger doctor, no pool, nor the vast array of other similarities.

Furthermore, the defendants never offered any explanation at all as to how the elements in my screenplay suddenly came to be in the cable series creator's script, and *no other verification of an independent creation made prior to my screenplay, apart from the aforementioned outline, was ever produced.*

On the other hand, I had kept meticulous records, a treasure trove of every single dated assignment, and all of the computer data I privately emailed to all of my teachers, as well as their private email responsess to me.

"The fact is," my lawyer said, "that Ms. Radin's script is the *first script in the history of the universe* to have combined the expressive elements she assembled to present a darkly comedic view of a middle-aged woman with terminal breast cancer." We researched this fact to make certain that was indeed correct, and my attorney began calling me "Little Grasshopper," inspired by the character in the popular *Kung Fu* series. According to all of the exhibits that existed in the court records we felt that we had proof of "access."

However, when I carefully studied the timeline evidence, I was shocked to see something that jumped out at me and broke my heart—the final betrayal.

Roughly 24 hours after I submitted my final work, as previously mentioned, to my teachers on December 2, 2008 at 2:48 p.m., the defense's own documents showed on December 3, 2008, at 4:33 p.m., *the first "pages" (basically a general outline) of a brand new script, which coincidentally contained numerous elements in my screenplay, was transmitted from one of the TV show producer's office to numerous other individuals apparently involved with the production.*

Nearing the end of the time in court, the judge to my right turned to the *defense* attorney and asked, "Is this infringement?" He promptly replied "No!"

The gavel came down before an objection could even be raised. But, why had she asked the defense attorney to answer that question for her and not my attorney, who would have resoundingly said "yes"? Again, it made no sense to me, but certainly seemed to substantiate Rodney's *Upstairs/Downstairs* philosophy.

The court's interpretation or understanding of "expressive elements" included only verbatim word-for-word copying, which is completely different from creative or dramatic writing as I taught it in my profession. Their interpretation did not include any of the above-mentioned similarities or any expressive elements.

Perhaps that's the way it should be in contract law, where exact word-to-word writing is crucial, but certainly not when it comes to creativity and artistic expression.

Ironically, as I turned to leave the courtroom, the appellate judge sitting all the way to my left stopped me.

"Ms. Radin," he said, "for what it's worth, your script was much better."

What he meant to be a genuine and compassionate gesture of understanding of the ordeal that I had just been through, though I appreciated it, it unfortunately felt like another stab in the heart.

Though their victory was a *legal* one, in my opinion, it certainly was not an honorable one. After losing the case, I was forced to pay $36,000 as "punishment."

What I learned about copyright law is that it allows for *more copy than rights*, and generally favors those who have the most money and power, as Rodney had warned me. In no way did I feel that justice had been served but rather, in the words of others who consoled me, that the entire legal process seemed little more than a "joke."

I knew beyond any doubt whatsoever that my attorneys were intelligent and dignified individuals who had done everything they could in this case. They will always remain my champions and Superheroes.

Nonetheless, I believe the cards were stacked against me and that the legal system, not my attorneys, failed me. And, in the end, it seemed to me that the copyright courts also reside "upstairs" with celebrities. I truly hope that the laws will be enlarged to cover this sort of issue, which is the only way justice can be served.

Two other strange things transpired around that time. First, the show was cancelled during the court proceedings. I assumed it was because of the court case and that they wanted to win before resuming the series.

The second was viewers seemed to notice a stark difference in the show from its beginning to its end. As one viewer put it, according to the August 14, 2013, review on Amazon.com, Season 3 of the cable series:

"This series started out as outrageously emotional and at the same time humorous and at times touching. It degenerated to ridiculous levels of craziness, the likes of which no family would consider remotely plausible, and definitely no longer funny."

Nevertheless, the show was brought back after I lost the court case for several wrap-up episodes, which even included the use of my title, "Quality of Life."

Oddly, in 2013, some months after I lost the case, Bonnie's teaching partner, whom I'll call Clyde, reached out to me online. Why he had waited until this moment and after the court case ended was beyond me. I had not heard from him since 2008, nor had I changed my email address. I was readily available through social media all that time, as well. I responded to Clyde about my ultimate disappointment with the writing program, *which I will always believe clearly gave away my script.* There is simply no other reasonable explanation that I can think of.

What I received back was even more astonishing. It was a legalistic letter that seemed to be a defense against something I had not even accused them of. Included in the letter were these words:

"I guess the reason we haven't been in touch with you earlier is that *we feared the worst about you* because we took you at your word about the seriousness of your condition."

Was Clyde calling me a liar because I had been fortunate enough to outlive my prognosis? Or, was he inferring they *thought I was dead* the day after I turned in my last assignments to them, so they never once even tried contacting me, until now?

I felt stunned knowing that the actions of those who

had betrayed me since my diagnosis were taken with the full knowledge that I was ill, and that my already difficult life would become infinitely more difficult because of those betrayals.

Regrettably, this seems to have bothered none of them at all.

12

Bucket List

Before the movie *Bucket List*, directed by Rob Reiner, came out in 2007, I had never heard of the term, though it has since entered the lexicon as the metaphor for the things we want to do before we die.

A while after my diagnosis, I went to see my gynecologist for a simple, routine test. When he walked in the room, he grabbed both of my hands and kissed me on the cheek. He seemed surprised to see me looking so reasonably well. I had complained to him for several years prior to my diagnosis about discomfort under my arm. Because of that experience and the one with my supposed "arthritis," I caution all women I know not to let things like that fall through the cracks.

"So, I imagine you and your husband are having lots of conversations, and making lists of things you want to do?"

Before you die was the implication.

"Of course," I said.

"Is he being supportive?" he asked.

"Absolutely!" I replied.

"Well, that's good to hear. Not of all of them are, these days."

I had not told him about my marital collapse, and I simply didn't want to go there. Before I left, he wrote down a few book titles that I might pick up for my husband if he developed trouble with what I was going through. I laughed to myself, but didn't let on. My eyes skimmed the list of books. I winced as I recognized one of the titles, which I had purchased for him, but went unread: *Breast Cancer Husband: How to Help Your Wife (and Yourself) during Diagnosis, Treatment and Beyond* by Marc Silver.

We chitchatted for a few moments.

"We'll send you a postcard and let you know if your test is normal, but everything looks good," he said.

"Thanks, but I will call to follow up just the same," I told him. I wasn't about to sit and wait for a postcard, ever again. I had learned too much about being a proactive patient. He kissed me on the cheek again before I left.

Then Bucket List appeared in the theatres. I began to consider what I would like to do, which I had abandoned for lack of health, energy, money, and a traveling companion.

I thought as always about Dr. Frankl's book, having tried to live up to his inspirational standards: remaining as productive as possible, trying to find meaning in my suffering, helping others, creating something special, and loving. I was confident that I'd done the best I could, though not perfect by any stretch of the imagination, but certainly the best I could.

I also pondered over and over again Ray Carver's poetic question, "Did you get what you wanted out of life?"

"Yes, absolutely!" I told myself. I took stock of some recent and wonderful experiences that gave me joy, especially my years of volunteer work with other cancer patients and sharing what I've learned about navigating the disease.

I recalled playing at the Jewish Homes for the Aged with my band for the last generation of Holocaust survivors. They loved the music. It was their music and what they had grown up with. They sang and danced as we played, celebrating life. It brought tears to my eyes to think that those of "the greatest generation," particularly the ones who struggled beyond imagination like Frankl, would in a matter of years all be gone from this world.

ⵝ ⵝ ⵝ

One late night when I couldn't sleep, I walked into my studio, surveying all of theatre stuff I had accumulated throughout my life. I opened a closet, which contained the numerous scripts from all the shows I had directed. Looking around the studio, each and every object represented a scene, a play, or a musical I had directed, or a child or adult I had worked with and had poured my heart and soul into.

Then I opened a large trunk, chock full of many hundreds of letters, cards, photos, and souvenirs from kids, their parents, and others with whom I had worked throughout the years.

Lara, who was visiting again—God bless her!—walked in on me.

"What are you doing?" she asked.

"What do I do with all this? I can't throw it away." My eyes became misty.

She sat next to me as we dug through the trunk and read through some of the handwritten notes.

"These are amazing," she said. She was right, they were, each and every one. "You've really had an impact… made a big difference in many lives."

Under one of the piles was a plaque, which I had received from the three hundred or so kids who were in a production of *Oliver!* that I directed at one of the many schools where I had worked. The parents had parodied the words to the song "I'd Do Anything." I remembered all the kids serenading me after the last performance. Lara and I sang it together.

"We'd do anything,
For you, Nanc, anything
For you mean everything, to us.
We know that
We'd go anywhere
For your smile, anywhere
For your laugh ev'rywhere,
We'd go
Learn a million words, anything
Learn to dance and sing, anything
Miss our recesses, everything
To rehearse with you,
You know that
We'd risk anything,
For this play everything
Yes we'd do anything
Everything for you!"

"Wow!" Lara said. "Don't worry, we'll figure out something wonderful to do with all of this."

ጸ ጸ ጸ

The longer I survived, the more I tried to do. I went back to school and spent three-plus years earning my writing certificate. Education has always been a critical part of my life. It made me feel alive to be stimulating my brain and not just treating my body.

When I was able, I planned some trips. It was too difficult for me to travel alone, and I had to time my trips between and around treatments. Every trip required a mask be worn on all flights, and an entire extra suitcase just of medications brought along.

I went to visit my sister and her family back east, all of whom I adore and who have always been wonderful to me. She and I planned a cruise to the Mediterranean. It was an easy way to travel, as it required no schlepping suitcases everywhere and, of course, the ship had a medical doctor onboard in case of emergency.

The cruise left from Venice, then went on to Dubrovnik, which was beautiful. It stopped in Turkey, which I had never been to and found fascinating.

Then we headed on to a favorite old friend, Greece. The year I studied in London, I traveled extensively throughout Europe, and camped alone on a beach in Greece. I made a little teepee out of my sleeping bag with towels and branches. There was a warm rain every night, but I happily slept in my tent for a week nonetheless. Every morning I would walk to a little café situated on a nearby farm and buy a bowl of freshly made Greek yogurt covered with honey. I played in the ocean during the day, and slept comfortably on the sand at night listening to the pitter-patter of the rain. It was heaven.

When Lara and I got to the island of Santorini, we rode donkeys up the steep switchback mountain path rather than hiking, which I did not have the energy to do. The donkeys were very slow going up, but on the way down, knowing they were going to be fed, it was like riding wild bucking broncos in a rodeo. We laughed hysterically and had an awesome time.

Two years later, I took my son to Israel. As before, a mask for the flight and a suitcase of meds were required. I had never been there before and, as a Jew, had always wanted to make that pilgrimage. We toured around the entire country on a bus for ten days. It was everything and more than I hoped for. I was overcome with emotion at Masada and in Jerusalem at the Western ("Wailing") Wall, in particular, when I saw the young male and female soldiers guarding it. They were impressive and committed young people. I believe all countries should offer military or community service opportunities for their young people. We also visited with my dear cousins who live there.

Next, my cousin Dan and I went to Amsterdam, my favorite city. I love the museums there, such as the van Gogh and the Rembrandt. The city is so walkable and people are amazingly friendly. The Anne Frank house, which I have been to several times, holds a special place in my heart. Having directed *The Diary of Anne Frank* a number of times, I was familiar with every square inch of the house and what occurred in each room. It has always been a deeply profound experience for me.

By that time, however, I noticed I was beginning to have much more difficulty walking, was falling a lot, and having trouble with balance. So, we also spent time in the cafés searching for the perfect puff of marijuana to alleviate my pain. We did a lot of sampling, and laughing, as we always do together.

When I returned home the problem got worse and worse, and eventually I found myself for the next several years relying upon a cane and mobility scooter. Allie would ride around on the scooter with me. I was tempted to get her goggles and a helmet like Snoopy. People would laugh and wave at us.

My daughter and I spent many weekends relaxing in the Wine Country, closer to home and easier for me, which we both loved to do.

Three years ago, I had surgery on my spine and nine months of grueling physical therapy that allowed me to walk, which I never thought I would do again. Of course, like my grandpa and father before me, dancing at a wedding would become my goal in life. And then, serendipitously, Jake announced he was getting married to a most special lady, Mari.

Next came the highlight of my life, a special trip to Cabo San Lucas with Dina, for Jake and his beautiful Mari's wedding. Most of my immediate and extended family (my elevator people and Superheroes) were there, which was icing on the cake.

As soon as the plane took off, I asked my daughter if she would like some champagne in celebration. I was elated. I ordered a bottle and three glasses. I poured all three glasses, and then took the extra glass back to her father, who had missed his flight and was sitting several rows behind us. I placed the glass of champagne on his tray and said "Mazel tov." I'd come too far to let anything or anyone stand in the way of this joyous occasion.

As I stood with my son and his beautiful bride under the chuppah, I knew then, as I always have, that nothing in the world meant more to me than living to see my children grow up, which God has graciously allowed me to do. Living through the major milestones of their lives became my goal and my reason for living.

As I stood there, I pictured the face of my grandfather struggling to dance at his grandson's wedding.

I also imagined the proud and delighted face of my father, who struggled to dance with me at my brother's wedding.

And then, finally...I danced with my son.

🎗🎗🎗

Now living in a delightful little place on the water that has the feel of a houseboat, I recently walked, Italian roast in hand, onto the deck and stared at the Bay, my Piscean panacea for whatever ails me. I thought back to all the difficult times and it suddenly occurred to me, that something I had never dared to dream of was fast approaching—another milestone.

With Stage 4 cancer, as many people unfortunately know, you live day-to-day, month-to-month, tumor markers–to–tumor markers, and every-treatment-to-every-treatment.

You bargain with God. I suspect even some atheists do, too. And, you beg for increments of time to live through special life events—especially those involving your children—graduations, engagements, weddings, and, perhaps, even the possibility of grandchildren. I have always been grateful beyond measure for each and every day that I have lived through—long enough to see my children grow to adulthood. What more could I possibly have asked for? Nothing.

I thought about the woman at the center of the story that I began writing so many years ago, although there were now two oddly similar stories. One was authentic, and one not.

My story was about an extensive struggle of a woman who had no idea what her future held in store, or if in fact there would even be a future. It looked ever so grim at the time and, in fact, I never had the opportunity to finish it in an authentic way. Those pages were missing. I had been waiting to see how my life and cancer unfolded before I wrote the ending, which I intended to be real, whether I lived or died.

Surviving for all these years, I realized that it now was more important than ever to finish my story, which had truly become a life-affirming one, living proof that miracles of modern medicine offer real hope.

I also realized that God had given me a certain ability to tell stories, as both a director and writer. I also understood what Frankl's idea of "finding meaning" really meant for me. I could share real hope with others who suffer from cancer and who worry about dying, or children, or experience abandonment, which unfortunately is more common these days. Perhaps, they too could find their way through the tunnel of darkness and come out the other side and into the sun.

I had to write it, all of it—the good, the bad and the ugly—as it finally became clear to me that the difficult ordeals of recent years had somehow strengthened me, and intensified my resolve to continue fighting.

Each and every painful betrayal had somehow unexpectedly and ironically made me stronger—what a sweet revenge. And, I smiled to think that was something that no court could ever take away. With these revelations, I decided to pick up where my story left off so many years ago.

I called my dear friend Vicky and asked if she wanted to take a walk. The path we walked parallels the beautiful

Bay, and the water looked like glass on that sunny day, while scores of boats were gliding across the glistening water. We could see both San Francisco and Sausalito from there, and the views, as always, were simply breathtaking.

We continued on, and I glanced to my left as we passed one of the schools where I had directed plays years ago when my kids where young. Recently visiting L.A., I had met with a former student, Daniel, who had played the wonderful role of Tevye for me in *Fiddler on the Roof* at that very school.

Now in his thirties, Daniel walked into the café. I didn't recognize his 6'2" frame or adult face, but he recognized me. As his eyes met mine he smiled, and I immediately recognized his familiar and delightful smile. He rushed over and stooped his tall, lean body to give me a long and heartfelt hug. It was wonderful to see him looking so well and happy, but I had to keep reminding myself that this man was the same talented young boy I taught so long ago.

He was excited to tell me about his work in the industry and how he loved living in L.A. Our wonderful reminiscences lasted for an hour or so before he had to get to work. Though it was difficult to eventually say "goodbye" to him, we promised to stay in touch, as we have. But before he left, he turned to me and said, "You know, Nancy, that play was the best thing that ever happened, not just to me, but for my entire family."

I choked up as I always do when I hear those kinds of wonderful comments. They represent what has always been the most meaningful part of teaching for me.

As Vicky and I continued on our walk I told her about my recent visit with Daniel, and how much my students have enriched my life. I also told her about my newfound determination to finish my story, and was giddy as I went on and on.

"That's fabulous. I am so proud of you." I felt blessed to have her as my friend. And then, I asked for her help.

"Sure, whatever you want," she replied.

"I want to plan a celebration."

"What are we celebrating?"

"I'm coming up on fifteen years." She stopped dead in her tracks, grabbed my arm and hugged me.

"Oh my God...has it really been that long? I've lost track of time."

"Who could've ever imagined, huh?" I shrugged.

"Absolutely no one," she replied.

"Well, you know," I told her, "nothing is promised when we come into this world, and there are no warranties in life."

"That's for sure," she said.

"There's more...I just found out that I 'm going to be a grandma this summer...a baby boy!" I shouted, beyond thrilled.

"Wow!" She screamed and hugged me again, this time so hard I thought I would pop.

"I've been luckier than I ever could have imagined." I could barely contain myself. After savoring the moment to its full extent, we eventually began to walk again.

"It's amazing you can say that. You've had so much to deal with all these years."

"Well, I've had no choice but to continue to put one foot in front of the other and keep marching forward. And, I'm glad I did."

"I glad you did too!" she said. "Hey, whatever happened to that woman in that TV show? I stopped watching in protest."

"Thanks. Me too. I hear they killed her." She looked stunned when I said that.

"What else could they do? The show was cancelled."

"How disappointing for all of the cancer patients who tuned in to watch. It didn't give them any hope."

"How else could it have ended?" I said. "You couldn't show her continuing to live unless the series continued, or there was some bizarre fast-forward to twenty years later. Or better yet, they could have added a contrived deus ex machina superpower that swoops in to save the day, like in Greek literature."

"I guess you're right. Remember the '80s series *Dallas*? They brought Bobby Ewing back to life a year after he died by turning the entire previous season into a delirious dream." We both chuckled when she said that. It seemed like a lifetime ago. Then we laughed about gorgeous Bobby standing in the shower.

"So, she really died in the show?"

"Yep, it's sadly ironic," I replied.

"Ironic? How?"

"What I stared writing, only four years into my diagnosis, was to give hope—because back then even four years was encouraging. Think about it. I'm still fighting, but the character in the TV show died."

"And look at you now." She smiled.

"What doesn't kill you makes you stronger, as they say. It's true. We are a lot tougher than we give ourselves credit for."

"Honestly, I'd rather have less strength and less to deal with."

"If only we were given that choice. But, incurable illnesses don't always end in death these days, you know. Some have become more chronic than fatal illnesses. Medicine has come a long way."

Then she asked the one question I truly had no real answer for.

"So, what do think has kept you alive all these years?"

"Ah...'there's the rub,' as Hamlet would say." Again, quoting my favorite Shakespeare play.

"You know I've always thrown it all up on the ceiling, whatever my body has reasonably been able to tolerate."

She'd heard me say that a million times before.

"Well something stuck, but what?"

"I really don't know. Maybe something I did...or something I didn't do, or maybe...it's just chance or luck?"

I truly was euphoric to be there on that beautiful day, walking that magnificent path, and with my dear friend.

"Whatever it is, and however long it lasts, I'll take it. I'm just happy that after all these years...I'm still here."

She gave me another hug. With that, I turned on the speaker to my phone and hit play.

Then, we sang and danced along the Bay...

"I've got all my life to live...

I've got all my love to give...

And I'll survive...

I will survive...

Hey, hey!"

Months later, I held my beautiful baby grandson in my arms.

The End

Acknowledgments

My deepest heartfelt appreciation and gratitude to all of the following Superheroes in my life:

To Phil Cousnieau for your inspirational writing wisdom and helping me to the finish line. To Jim Shubin my book designer, and David Greitzer the cover photographer.

To Mark Burstein for your copyediting expertise, Sam Barry for the big push, and the wonderful Book Passage.

To Dr. Linnea Chap, Dr. Catherine Clark-Sayles, and Dr. Roger Weinhouse for saving my life and gift of the last fifteen years. And, to the doctors and staff of The Revlon/UCLA Breast Center, UCLA Jonsson Comprehensive Cancer Center Department of Radiation Oncology, Beverly Hills Cancer Center, UCSF Breast the Jewish Family and Children's Services, Monica Lopez, Jan (Janquenette) Austin, and Marlene Averetta Hodges.

To Rafael Chodos, the late Hillel Chodos, and Laura Godorecci for your wonderful counsel, support, and patience.

To Catherine Hand, Don Weinhouse, Vicki Israel, Marilyn Weinhouse, Alison Von Lackum, Joely Fisher, Jane Pitts, Steve Rose, Peggy Schmotter, Sher Honchariw, Dave Heller, Liz Lewellen, David Murray, Jack Barron, Lynn Weisman, Arlene Fishbach Janelle Brady, Pat Agnitch,

Erin Braxton, Michael and Jonathan, Annelies Atchley, the late Dr. Bill Atchley, Jackie O'Neill, and the late John Ingle, for the many ways you have enriched my life and supported me.

To my entire Smith Family for your eternal love and laughter.

And finally, to my sister, my brother, my children and my baby grandson. I love and adore you!

Thank you all from the very bottom of my heart.

Nancy

About the Author

Nancy F. Radin has been living with metastatic cancer and been a peer counselor for 15 years. She is a theatre teacher, director and writer who began her teaching career at Beverly Hills High School, has taught at the American Conservatory Theater (A.C.T.) in San Francisco, and other schools. Nancy directed her own community theatre for many years, has written many original short plays, and is currently writing a book/play on Shakespeare. She splits her time between Los Angeles and San Francisco.

Made in the USA
Coppell, TX
17 March 2023

14367508R00128